SHOES AND CHEESE
THE BOONETOWN CHRONICLES

BOBBY EVERS

To Amy, for telling me I should write, and
to Frances, who wouldn't let me stop.

Acknowledgements

For invaluable editing, encouragement, and advice, thank you Carolyn German and Wordsmith Collaborative. And always, my heartfelt thanks to each and all of the friends, family, and clients who continue to support my creative endeavors.

Contents

Introduction   1

Barbara Mandrell in the Local News   3

Shoes and Cheese   13

The Joy of Not Cooking   21

Joe and Lorena   27

The Bathroom Pro's   35

Great Heights   41

Beef Stew   53

Tom   61

Here's Your Sign   69

The Tin Man   75

Help Wanted?   85

Shoes and Weddings   89

Don Jackson, Loaded Gun   99

Oh, Shit   111

The Letter   119

Alfie's Lunch Box   127

Mom   141

Making Do   155

Taxi Driver   165

And Sew It Goes   169

One of the Guys   177

It's All in the Design   185

A Merry Little Christmas   201

INTRODUCTION

I like observing people. I just find people interesting, especially people who take a few detours along the way. I watch...and wonder.

Once, while I was out eating brunch, I saw a man riding his unicycle down the street, while carrying a bicycle on his shoulder. I wondered.

I wondered too, at my podiatrist's office, if the seventy-five-year-old woman sitting next to me wore her Britney Spears t-shirt and carried her Britney Spears handbag everywhere, or just when she went to the doctor? Nothing wrong with that, I just wanted to understand her thought process.

And I used to wonder why I kept a file of random stuff: articles, and ads, and photos, and notes... things I found interesting. But now I know: to use to tell these stories.

These stories are about a place I call Boonetown and some of the folks who live there. They are stories about people who have made me smile, shaped me, and intrigued me. This is the way I remember the people and events, although some might remember them differently. But you don't have to be from Boonetown to recognize the people in these pages. Because, as it turns out, *The Boonetown Chronicles* isn't just about me and my hometown, it's about everyone's. So here goes.

I hope you enjoy your stay.

Barbara Mandrell in the Local News

The Boonetown Times is still my source for local news, even in this online age. It keeps me up to date on all the latest fund raisers, school sporting events, meth lab seizures and of course, obituaries. As I get older, I find that checking the obituaries takes on new significance, and I also worry that we seem to have an alarming number of meth labs in Boone County.

Pages one through three are usually what I call the reliable news. Then you get past those into the society pages with the articles contributed by various local columnists; those, I would say, are less factual. Over the years I have found some of the stories in the paper puzzling, and they do leave me (very often) wanting more, even from the ones on the front or second page. I know it takes a lot of words to fill a weekly paper, so I give them the benefit of the doubt. But some weeks I do wonder if the editor-in-chief was on vacation.

For instance, once I saw a headline that said,

"Thief Takes Laxatives and Runs"

Were they trying to be funny? Well, apparently not, because there was a full article about someone in a drug store stealing a bunch of Ex-lax and running for the door. But the headline just made me feel a little cheated. I wanted more from the article. I needed a punchline. Where did he run to? The bathroom? A getaway car? More details, please.

And people in Boonetown pay for some of the strangest ads. Space in newspapers, even local papers, is not cheap. So I'm not sure why a person would pay good money for such odd notices. This one particular ad was on the inside of the front page, about the size of an index card. I still have it if you want a copy, and this is an exact quote:

"NOTICE: Chubby Clayton's 78th birthday party on September 16th has been cancelled due to lack of interest shown by family, friends and co-workers."

Well, damn. Poor Chubby. There was also a picture in the ad of a very sad looking older man with messy hair. I assume it was Chubby. I had not been invited to Chubby's birthday party because I didn't really know Chubby, nor had I previously seen an invitation in the paper inviting me to his party, so I wasn't sure if it was a joke or not. But I felt really bad for Chubby. Had he pissed off his family and friends? Was he a mean person? Was Chubby even a real person?

We were really into this cancelled-party news in the office. My co-workers made calls to friends to see if anyone knew Chubby. We were thinking of having Chubby a party to make up for the cancelled one. I think we could have gotten half the town to come. People all over were feeling bad for Chubby. But would Chubby even show? Should we take out an ad asking Chubby to come to his own party? I had become invested in Chubby and I didn't even know him. I needed more information.

I never got any answers.

Another favorite headline in the local paper was a

4

few years ago. I'm quoting exactly:

"6-pack Shields Woman from Stabbing Attack"

Now that is a headline. They had me at "6-pack." The article went on to explain that a woman owed her healthy condition to the fact that she was holding a six-pack of beer when she was attacked by her neighbor. The forty-two-year-old woman was in her yard, going into her home, when her neighbor came running from across the street with a knife in her hand. The sixty-three-year-old neighbor raised her hand, holding the knife and bringing it downward in a stabbing motion when the first woman lifted the six-pack of beer she was holding, blocking the stab. Can't you just see that? In slow motion? I could. I wish I didn't jump to conclusions, but I just wanted to put a picture with this story.

What did these women look like? What were they wearing? The paper needed to give us more. Not a single photo or description was included. I had to come up with my own. I feel like the woman with the six pack of beer was probably in her shopping clothes, maybe stretch pants in a camo pattern, a tank top with a beer logo, and some flowers tattooed on her shoulder...and definitely wearing flip flops. And I'm thinking since the woman with the knife was at home, maybe she was just casual: in cut-off shorts, a t-shirt, and maybe her roots needed to be touched up, badly. And I feel sure she was smoking.

See, this is so unfair of me. I should not jump to conclusions. They could have both been in Dior suits and Jimmy Choo heels. But I'm just betting they were not. I feel like it was hot out since tempers were flaring. Maybe they were fighting over a man. Yes, I bet they were, and I bet he was a handsome fellow.

Once again, it just seems like the investigative reporting falls very short. There was no mention of the motive, or what happened to the beer, or how many cans were lost, or what happened to either of these women, only that one woman's life had been saved because she was carrying a six pack of beer and the other was being charged.

Bill Davis was a local man who contributed columns to *The Boonetown Times* on a regular basis, about anything from politics to garbage service, as I recall. Apparently, Bill was lonely and also needed some help around the house, so he placed his own ad looking for company. I clipped it and saved it. It said:

"WANTED: A house mate for Bill Davis. No sex, cold beer. Will provide or share all cost of survival. Would like someone who can mow the yard, grow tomatoes, can cook, hang clothes to dry and drive for groceries. Not wanted are drug addicts, super Christians, or those with Domestic problems. Apply in Person."

Now that my friends, is how you write an ad.

You know what he wants, you know what he needs, and you get a very good idea of what living with him might be like. Indentured servant, maybe, or household grunt-worker, but at least there is no sex involved and he's not sugar coating anything. And yet, once again, no follow-up. I've always wondered who applied in person. Did he find someone? Maybe the woman with the knife when she got out of jail? She probably needed a place to live. I think she could hold her own with Bill Davis.

So, this brings me to *The Boonetown Time*'s gossip columnists. I'm not sure about them either. I don't think they do any fact checking at all. For instance, here is a prime example. It happened a long time ago, but you'll get my point.

One of my best friends got into a little incident on

Christmas night. This was before cell phones were in constant use and before PETA was spray painting people's fur coats. Maggie and her best friend Shelby had received fur coats for Christmas that year and they were at home lounging in them, still in their pajamas, when Maggies's husband, Randy, got an idea. Randy loved to buy and sell cars, and this particular year he had bought an old used limousine. He always wanted to be famous himself. He thought he was born to be a country music star, but sadly, his voice had proved him wrong.

Now, you need to know that Barbara Mandrell was quite a famous country music singer at this time and had been on a weekly television show for several years, but the show had ended, and she had retired back to Nashville. My friend Maggie had been told a couple of times that she looked a bit like Barbara, they both had shoulder length blonde hair, but Maggie was taller.

Since it was Christmas, Maggie, Shelby, and their husbands decided to go for a ride to see some of the Christmas decorations they had heard about over in Montery, a nearby community. Of course, they took the limousine, Randy drove, and Shelby's husband sat in the front passenger seat. Maggie and Shelby rode in the back. They didn't even bother changing out of their pajamas. They just buttoned up their new fur coats, thinking they would be in the car the entire time.

It was about a thirty-minute drive over to Montery. There was a large, impressive Christmas display that this particular homeowner had set up on his property. They had a barn decorated with a nativity scene inside, complete with live animals and festive displays of lights and decorations all around their house. It was set up in such a way that you could drive through and around the property on their driveway, and then exit on another driveway.

When the couples arrived, quite a line of cars was out on the road, waiting to get into the driveway. One of the men directing traffic saw the limousine and immediately came running over to ask who was inside. The thought must have been that since they were only about seventy-five miles south of Nashville, and in a limousine, there might be country stars inside. Apparently some country music stars had been down to see the lights previously, so it was a reasonable assumption.

The man knocked on the window, and immediately asked if a country music star was in the back. Maggie's husband couldn't let the opportunity pass.

He said, "Oh, no sir, I'm not at liberty to say who's in the car, I mean Miss Mandrell instructed me, I mean, I was instructed…I mean…I'm sorry…I meant…I mean I'm not permitted to say and you didn't hear me say that…please sir?"

The man immediately lit up like a Christmas tree and said, "Oh sir, just one moment, just a moment." With that he radioed another man (who was also directing traffic) and suddenly cars were being directed off the road into the ditches. Other cars were being forced to park or to move, and within minutes the path was clear, and Maggie and her party were driving up to the house like the VIP's they were.

When they arrived up at the house, they noticed most everyone was getting out and taking a look at the decorations up close. They felt there would be no harm in taking a quick look around. They got out, and walked over to the front of the house, where a guestbook had been left for visitors to sign-in and list where they were visiting from. So, they did that too.

Then, as they were walking away from the house Maggie told Randy, "I don't know what came over me, but when I picked up the pen, my hand wrote Barbara Mandrell in the most beautiful handwriting over three lines of the guest book."

Around that time, they began to hear a clatter in the distance. Maggie could make out snippets of what they were saying like, "There they are!", "Oh, I see Barbara," and "There is her limo!"

The phrase that popped into Maggie's head was simply, "Run!"

They briskly walked toward the limo, and were able to duck inside just as the homeowners were getting near. Obviously, there had been communication from the traffic men, because the homeowners were now heading over, saying they wanted to meet Miss Mandrell.

Maggie's husband was cranking the engine and it wasn't turning over. He probably should have bought a newer model. Finally, with a last moan the engine started. And, even though the folks were trying to get them to stop, Maggie's husband waved and said "I've got to get these ladies back to Nashville!"

They were thankful for tinted windows.

They weren't sure if they had been figured out or not. That is, until a couple of days later when they got *The Times*.

Lucy Green wrote a weekly gossip column which covered weddings and teas and Christmas parties and the like. She also reported about Boonetown residents who had made the trip over to Montery to see the Smith's big Christmas display. It was good filler, and I'm pretty sure she was paid by the word. But in this particular column there was exciting news. The Smith's had called her to report that on Christmas night, country music sensation Barbara Mandrell and her entourage had driven all the way down from Nashville to view their decorations. The article went on to say that Barbara could not have been nicer, and had gotten out of the car and visited with the family and signed autographs. "It's just wonderful when someone famous turns out to be so down-to-earth," she concluded. Turns out the homeowners with the Christmas display were just as big liars as Maggie and her husband.

I am reminded of one of the other gossip columnists in Boonetown, Nancy Rutrell. Patricia, my office assistant at the time, had become totally engrossed by Nancy's columns. Nancy was much more direct than Lucy. Her columns could get quite lengthy. (I think she was paid by the word as well.) Sometimes, Nancy didn't really have a lot of finesse. I noticed this as I began to read her column regularly. I had never read a local column faithfully before. But the whole office was now really into Nancy's column, so I started reading too, and then we would discuss. One thing Patricia and I both loved was that Nancy didn't mind calling out someone for behavior she didn't approve of, right there in her column. Often, it was her own children. Sometimes there would be veiled comments. Other times, not so veiled.

Nancy Rutrell was a bargain watchdog. In her column, she always mentioned when she was able to get a two-for-one burger deal at Hardee's, or when Senior Day was at the Sonic. She was a huge supporter of the town's goings on, and always an attendee of church covered dish dinners, square dances, local bluegrass music, and Senior Day at the county fair. If there was a bargain in town, Nancy was all over it. And she always posted pictures from each and every event. She reported who brought the baked

10

beans, and whose fried chicken was the best.

Unfortunately, Nancy began to have some fairly serious health problems, as did her husband. But instead of feeling sorry for herself, she took it as an opportunity to write about the details of every doctor's visit, hospital stay and blood test. If she had an MRI, you knew what color the inside of the big metal tube was. She would go into detail about the time her car wouldn't start in the hospital parking lot or the time the cafeteria left the Jello off her lunch tray. Nancy was thorough.

One week, Nancy was writing about her family Christmas activities. Right off the bat, I could tell she wasn't pleased. She said that all of her children, *except* one, had been home to see her over the holidays. (It didn't take great powers of deduction to figure which one if you read the rest of the column.) She wanted all the kids at home so they could go to the cemetery together, and put the Santa hat on Daddy's tombstone. Because, she said, "Daddy always was Santa." Daddy apparently was Nancy's first husband and the father of her children.

She wrote that when they got to the cemetery, to put the Santa hat on his tombstone, things were amiss. She said, "There was a dead armadillo laying there, just a stinking." Then she noticed on the other side of his grave, there was a screwdriver just lying there. She went on to say, "I suspected foul play, but I never was able to prove anything."

Patricia and I spent a good deal of time speculating about who she called to investigate the crime scene. I'm not sure where the cemetery was, so I can't be sure about the jurisdiction. Besides, I wasn't sure who you would ask for when you called in to report the crime. The wildlife homicide division maybe? But knowing Nancy, she spoke to someone

11

about it, and I either missed the follow-up column or she didn't post the details. Could have been a gag order in place, I suppose.

I've gotten a lot of pleasure from reading *The Boonetown Times* over the years. I still wonder about Chubby and his uninterested family, friends and co-workers, and if Bill Davis found a housemate, and if Barbara Mandrell ever actually saw the Christmas lights.

I also do a lot of wondering on my weekly trips up the interstate to Nashville. Because I often see dead armadillos lying on the side of the road, "just a stinking". And I can't help but wonder, you know, if there had been foul play.

Shoes and Cheese

Sometimes I wonder if people in small towns are just smarter than big city folks, because they seem to figure out lots of interesting ways to make money.

Take Boonetown for instance. I love how our local merchants adapt to the needs of their customers, expanding and adding new product lines to increase sales. Sure, it creates some odd combinations, but does that really matter?

I guess I have just taken Lenny D's for granted ever since it opened. The sign reads, "Lenny D's Check Cashing, Tanning Beds and Mulch."

This is truly one stop shopping. Countless are the times I needed to cash a check, pick up a load of mulch, and get a tan in the same afternoon.

Of course, we have a couple of other places that offer check cashing and tanning. I think that's pretty common. But throw in the need for some mulch and Lenny D's is the only place. I guess the success of those services prompted him to expand since he now offers tattoos and doughnuts as well. Just sort of adds a whole new dimension to the mulch and tanning excursion.

Brown's Department Store has been in business

for years selling Levi's, tuxedos, and artificial funeral flowers. During my childhood, I remember making the fall trip to Brown's to get my going-back-to-school Levi's. It was the only place you could get a thirty-inch waist by thirty-eight-inch length jean. (Yes, I was tall and skinny.) Recently, they moved to a new location and added used cars to the mix. A natural fit I thought.

Doesn't every Muffler Shop have a Snow Cone Stand? Ours does, but only in warmer months.

One day I was driving out to the Boonetown suburbs to look at a job site and I saw a sign on a small building, kind of a garage, I guess.

The sign said: "Larry's Used Tires and Colognes."

How had I missed this? I almost stopped to check it out, but I was short on time. I will one day.

Growing up, I remember riding my bike down to the store at the corner of the block, every day after school. It was one of our first convenience stores. They had cold drinks, and some groceries, and a few other basics. I would take a quarter, get a coke and a Payday candy bar, and get some change back. (I just realized how old that makes me sound.)

Nelson Harwood owned the store and was a constant presence behind the little counter. He would sell single cigarettes...on credit...to the people in the "poor folks" section of town. They would come in and buy two cigarettes, or maybe three, until their check came in. He sold other merchandise "on credit" too, but it's the cigarettes that I always remember. I guess people must have their smokes.

One time I had to take the local taxi in Boonetown. This is a town that only has one taxi. Well, it did *then*, anyway. Now we have none. But we used to have this one taxi. That's one taxi in total, not one taxi service with several taxis, just one old, worn-out taxi. Period.

Grimsley was the driver. I know this because he was the only taxi driver in town.

It took a brave and desperate soul to ride with Grimsley. I was desperate the day I got in his cab, for sure. My car was in the shop and I had to get to an appointment. Grimsley chain smoked the entire time. The cigarette smoke and nicotine stains sent me into an allergy-induced coma. Thank God it was a short trip. I was sick for a week. Riding with Grimsley wasn't cheap either. I think he tacked on some extra fees to cover cigarettes.

Around that time a semi-famous novelist bought a large country home in Boonetown to get away from it all. Then the big flood of 1998 hit. It completely washed away her driveway and access to her home, leaving all her vehicles parked uselessly in her driveway. She had to cross her washed out driveway on foot and then depend on Grimsley and his taxi for her transportation everywhere...for weeks. Said she could have written a book after that experience. No shit.

Then, in the early 2000's when Lenny D's business was really taking off, a strange phenomenon hit Boonetown. Apparently, someone thought they could make a lot of money in the luxury travel business. (It was a good thought I guess, because after my taxi experience, any other form of travel was welcome.)

At that time, we had a population of around 13,000. No concert venues, no sports arenas, no formal functions or red carpets to walk.

Suddenly, we had four limousine services.

I don't mean one business that had four limousines. I mean we had four different businesses that had limousines for rent. All at the same time.

You could drive down the highway from Wal-Mart to McDonalds and see shined-up limos sitting all over the place. Where were they going? I had no idea. It seems everyone was suddenly providing limousine services. We boasted of our Radio Shack and Limousine Service, the Diamond Hut Jewelry Store and Limousine Service, and the Tent Party Rental Place and Limousine Service. Then there was another one that was just a Limousine Service on its own. I don't know how it survived all on its own like that, but they worked it out.

Was there some underground black-tie world in Boonetown I knew nothing about? Or had our Amish community finally gotten tired of hitching up the horse to the buggy every time they want to go to McDonalds for a Big Mac? I must say that, looking back, it truly was the golden age of travel for Boone County.

It's a real shame the semi-famous novelist lost her driveway prior to the limousine era in Boonetown. She could have gone everywhere in style. She only missed it by a couple of years.

My doctor back then also got in on the Boonetown-multiple-revenue-streams idea. He was an ear, nose and throat specialist by trade, and treated allergies. He had moved into Boonetown and bought a house, and built up a sort of fortress around it…lots of trees and fencing. There were five, big, mean dogs patrolling the property as well. He was primarily an ENT, but I suppose he wasn't making enough money in that specialty. Turns out that on Wednesdays, he was a plastic surgeon, doing tummy tucks, breast enhancements, and liposuction in the same office. I could only imagine how much that added to his bottom line (while simultaneously decreasing his patients bottom line).

He did these procedures just down the hall from where I got my allergy shots. My sister thought I was crazy to let him take my tonsils out, but I had been to several other doctors and no one would. They said I was too old. But I was sick all the time and I needed to get something done. He took my tonsils out and, I must say, it was the best I had felt in years. Then he opened a skin care spa next door where they would tattoo on permanent make-up as well as do your nails. (He was talking about opening a deli too, but wasn't everyone? I even thought about it for a while.) In Boonetown, he fit right in.

I remember one morning in the Boonetown post office, I was picking up the morning mail and I noticed this lovely older lady. I'd guess she was in her late sixties, or early seventies. She was walking across the parking lot toward the side door. On the last day of July, in small-town Tennessee, she was wearing a full-length evening gown, complete with sequin bodice and flowing chiffon skirt. It complimented her neck brace and wig nicely, and her make-up was flawless. She was flowing in the breeze. It was a nice, expensive dress and she had well-coordinated accessories. Even the neck brace was in a matching tone. She was assisting herself with a cane as she walked.

The thing I found most interesting about her was that she was not in the least self-conscious about the fact that she was just a tad overdressed for the post office. (In Boonetown you usually don't see evening gowns until at least four p.m.) As I waited in line, I tried to think of a scenario involving waking up, putting on your neck brace and your new evening gown, and then going to mail a letter. None came to mind immediately. Could she have been on her way to get married? Was one of our many limos waiting in the parking lot to take her away to the Oscars, or the Grand Ole Opry? I didn't see a limo circling the block or waiting in the parking lot. Was she on her way to Lenny D's for a doughnut or a tattoo?

Upon returning to work, I asked for help. The answer was so obvious. The neck brace, the cane... my brother figured it out right away. She was on her way to court. She must have been in an accident and was heading to court expecting an insurance settlement. I could just hear her lawyer telling her to "dress real pretty for the Judge." And she did. You see, I told you, people in Boonetown just figure out ways to make money.

During this golden age of entrepreneurialism and luxury transportation in Boonetown, another mode of transportation popped up that really had me worried.

It was these battery-powered wheelchairs.

Suddenly they were everywhere. Including on busy streets.

Don't get me wrong, I have the deepest sympathy and concern for a person who is in a wheelchair. But a few of them act like they think they are driving little cars.

This one mean girl will just run you over in the post office, and smile at you while you are grabbing your ankle to stop the gushing blood. Then she drives it right down the center of a busy street on her way to the next stop. On any given day you will meet her on the four-lane highway or crossing a busy intersection sitting in her chair just as casually as if she were at home in her recliner watching television.

I think she has confidence.

She has a boyfriend who also has a motorized wheelchair. A little newer model it seems, but he can't keep up with her. He's always about a car's length behind.

I would keep my distance from her too.

I don't know how they could be making money while driving around like this, but it's Boonetown after all, and I am sure they thought of something.

Sadly, the golden age of luxury transportation was short-lived. Almost as suddenly as they came to town, after only a decade or so, I found myself asking, "Where have all the limos gone?" The Radio Shack closed, and the Diamond Hut no longer had their fleet parked out front. Maybe the party scene dried up? I still don't know. I just know that suddenly I was very worried about what I might do if a prom invitation popped up in my mailbox.

I haven't seen the mean girl or her boyfriend in years. Maybe they bought a limo and headed out of town.

But the spirit of entrepreneurialism is still strong in Boonetown. Lenny D's is still around, and so is Brown's Department Store. And, I just had a snow cone over at the muffler shop.

A few weeks ago, I was asked to remodel an old building downtown on the square. "It will fit perfectly in Boonetown," I thought. The owner said that it will have a pharmacy, guns, knives, and ammo, as well as homemade jams, jellies and yes, you guessed it, a deli.

Recently an insurance salesman came by my office to present an insurance proposal. I noticed he looked pale and could use a little sun. So, I gave him directions to Lenny D's. I also told him about some of the other local businesses in Boonetown. He began telling me about some of the stores in his hometown. He said they had an interesting store there that sold only shoes and cheese.

I thought, "Wow! Thank God I don't live in a town that has a strange store like that." Shoes and cheese, now that is just odd.

The Joy of Not Cooking

Years ago, I was asked to write something about cooking for this cool little regional magazine. Asking someone like me to write an article about food is, well, a bit risky.

I would assume they were looking for something along the lines of my favorite recipe, or an article about the joys of cooking. I am afraid you will find none of that with me.

I hate cooking. Loathe it.

Many years had passed since I made any serious attempts to cook a meal. I think the editors, like so many people that know me, jumped to the wrong conclusion that I am a great cook because I am very creative. But I never found cooking worth the time and energy. It always seemed like so much work, and then it was all just gone.

Unfortunately, when COVID-19 hit, my worst nightmare became a reality: I had to cook.

My range top has this really annoying clock that flashes, demanding to be reset every time the power goes off. So in order to avoid unnecessary time in the kitchen resetting the clock, I always keep the breaker for the range in the off position. I only have to turn it back on when my sister would visit for Thanksgiving so that she could cook the dressing. I never cook.

I think that one of the big reasons I don't like cooking is the grocery shopping. To me, going to the grocery store falls somewhere between fingernails scratching on a chalkboard and water torture. I figure if it isn't in Walgreen's food section, I don't need it. It's kind of a domino effect: one thing calls for another and another and another. If you cook regularly, you have stuff like ingredients, and spices, and things that are still in date. But if you don't cook regularly, you need everything. Even the things that you do have on hand are usually out of date, so it's back to the store again. And before you know it, you've spent about a hundred and fifty dollars to make a tuna casserole.

Unfortunately, once every couple of years, I do have to make the trek to Kroger for my blizzard and sick food. That's the limited supply of food I keep in the house in case we have one of those once-every-hundred-year blizzards that snows you in for several days. I buy frozen dinners and canned soups. Chicken noodle for illness and vegetable beef for the blizzards. This way I am covered in the event of heavy snowfall or major stomach virus.

Only problem is, I thought that canned food lasted longer.

Just the other day I was checking my inventory (when the weather forecast looked foreboding) and I noticed that most of my soup cans had "sell-by" dates that had long since passed. Apparently, we haven't had a blizzard in a decade and my stomach has been holding up quite well. But really, shouldn't canned soup last a little longer than four or five years? I had to completely restock.

So in between blizzards and stomach viruses, I eat out or get carry-out. A lot. If it comes through a window wrapped in white paper or in a Styrofoam box, that's fine with me. Or if a man dressed in black brings it to my table, even better. As a single person, this system just seems to work for me. And when I'm lucky, I find some really great restaurants that go beyond good food and service. With those places, I sort of fall in love. But I can be fickle. I still like to eat around.

I know which restaurants have the best of this or that, and the best times to eat to avoid the rush. I may not know how to cook, but I can damn sure place an order with the best of them. I figure that, considering the amount of waste I had back in the days when I did try to cook, I am not really spending that much more money. I mean, everything seemed to go bad before I could cook it.

I guess my favorite thing about eating out is the social aspect. I have made some great friends from the staff at my favorite eateries, and I just love having a long conversation with a good friend over dinner... and not having to run to the kitchen every five minutes.

I have this favorite Italian restaurant in New York right in the theater district. I eat there at least once or twice every trip. Beyond the fact that the food is amazing, the waiters remember me and even know what I am going to order. Even when I haven't been there in six or eight months, they still greet me and ask if I am going to have the salmon with roasted vegetables. And I usually do because it's the best I've had anywhere. I love that.

Some people—you know the type, those that cook everything from scratch—are always super critical. They will send their food back at O'Charley's because it isn't cooked just so. Those people often question why I don't cook. Well, as far as I am concerned, my eating habits are supporting the economy and providing jobs.

People are also quick to point out that restaurant food is less healthy than home cooking, and I am sure they are correct. But I think they are overlooking one important point. When you eat out, you get one portion and when it is gone, that's it, you are done. People who cook at home usually have leftovers and thus the problem begins. There it is in the refrigerator, calling your name all night. So instead of one portion of meatloaf, by the end of the evening, you might eat three. I know I would, but *my* left overs are over at Ted's Montana Grille, and they aren't at home taunting me all night. The fantastic cheesecake that I would have had one piece of at the restaurant would be half gone before I went to bed. I have no willpower and I know it. On those rare occasions that good, home-cooked food finds its way into my home, I can't leave it alone. If it is not there, I never even think about eating. So, you see, it's really a health issue for me. Not cooking is surely adding years to my life.

Or I should say, that was my plan. It had worked for fifty years or so and I was fine with it. I was from a family of good cooks and if I wanted some home cooking, I could find it. Otherwise, I would depend on the kindness of strangers. That is, until COVID and quarantine.

Suddenly restaurants were closed and everything changed. I could not count on my regular places. I was forced to switch on the breaker to my range and dust off my skillets. I always knew it would take something big to get me cooking, and I guess a global pandemic is about as big as you can get.

Suddenly strange things were happening. I had

no room in my pantry. The ingredients I would pull out of the fridge were still actually in date. And I was throwing away empty containers. I was actually using all the food up before it went bad. This had never ever happened before.

And you know what? To my utter amazement, my cooking skills started to improve. I began to really enjoy some of the food I was making for myself. I was even making things that required more than three ingredients. I started to challenge myself a bit. I started doing strange things like asking friends for recipes, and would hear unnatural phrases come out of my mouth like, "And what temperature did you cook your snapper at?"

And I know you are thinking that I am about to say that I finally began to love cooking. Well, then, you would be exactly *wrong*.

Hated it! Hated every minute of it! Still hate it. I could not wait for my favorite restaurants to reopen, even if only for takeout. They needed my support and I would not let them down. I couldn't meet my friends out for dinner, which I still miss terribly, but I could go eat by myself ten feet away from everyone and at least get a good meal, or pick up something on the way home.

I hit the wall. The kitchen wall. Things started going bad in the refrigerator again. I started throwing out half full containers of cheese or eggs. I knew it was time. I flipped the breaker back off.

Because of the COVID quarantine, my favorite restaurant in NYC was closed for six months. They finally reopened at twenty-five percent capacity, but I so worry they won't make it. I want to go have dinner there and see a show as soon as possible. I want that delicious food, and I want that salmon dish, and I want to tell them that I missed them. And I want to see if they remember me. I think they might.

A few years ago, when my father was very ill and in the nursing home after having a massive heart attack, he would not eat. He simply had no desire for food. This is a man who loved to cook and lived to eat, so we knew things did not look good. The staff therapist had the idea to take him into the dining room and seat him at a table with a plate and utensils like he would have used at home. The idea made sense. He had never eaten a meal from a bed tray. He always ate at the dining table and was used to my mother's amazing home cooking. Surely this would trigger his memory and he would start eating. It did not.

I was there with a friend of mine observing all of this. I turned to her and said, "If I am ever in this same situation, and lose the desire to eat, put me in the car and take me through a drive-thru window. That ought to do it."

JOE AND LORENA

When I was little, I loved it when my parents went out for the evening. Even better, when they went out of town.

My babysitter was a woman named Lorena, and I absolutely adored her. This was one thing my brother, sister, and I could agree on. We were all crazy about Lorena and her brother Joe. I thought she was old at the time, but she was probably only in her late fifties. She was small in stature, kept her hair cropped at chin length, always wore simple little shift dresses, and already had vision problems. I think she had cataracts, but I also remember there was something else causing her vision to degenerate. I believe it was hereditary. She never complained though. She just kept her great big magnifying glass by her chair. She would use it to search the dictionary when she was stumped by one of her word puzzles. She had never married, and lived with her younger brother Joe. Joe was a house painter and wallpaper hanger. He supported them because Lorena had spent years staying at home and taking care of her bedridden, blind mother. Joe was average height, stocky, bald-headed, and was always sporting a smile. To supplement their meager income, Lorena would babysit at night.

They lived in a very small, but very charming, Victorian "gingerbread" house with only four rooms or so. It was just a half a block east, and two short blocks north of my childhood home. I loved that I could ride my bike over to see them. They both loved children, perhaps because they didn't have any, but mainly because it was just their nature. They always had time to stop and listen and pay attention to whatever I had to say. They both exuded a joyful love of life.

The obvious hardships they had suffered were never mentioned, only their appreciation for friends and for every new day. Joe had never married either, and he lived in the small attic bedroom without air conditioning. Lorena slept in the only bedroom downstairs after her mother passed away.

I cannot remember a time in my childhood without Joe and Lorena. Some other kids in the neighborhood got to know Lorena as a babysitter, but not like I did.

Joe and Lorena were a Saturday night staple at our house. They were my mom and dad's best friends and were at our house for dinner at least one, sometimes two, nights a week. Lorena always brought some things she had made, Mom would make the rest, and sometimes Dad would grill. We ate good. Really good. This was before we knew about high cholesterol (and all that other bad stuff) and changed the way we ate. So everything was still full of butter, and cream, and all the good stuff.

After dinner, everyone would move into the den where Dad and Joe would watch *Lawrence Welk*. They both loved that show so much, even if it was wholesome to the point of corny. They both loved the music of that era, and it was great music. Dad and Joe had both served in the military. After Dad got out of the Air Force and married Mom, he and Mom and Joe and Lorena became the closest of friends.

I think it was Joe that first introduced Dad to golf. Before that, Dad had been big into bowling and fishing. But after he met golf, that all changed. He began golfing at least twice a week and did so for the rest of his life. Joe was one of his foursome regulars on Saturday. So on Saturday, he and Dad would golf. Then Joe and Lorena would come over for dinner.

The only problem was by the time *Lawrence Welk* came on the air, both Joe and Dad had golfed, eaten...and drank. They would begin to nod off during the show they loved so much. Especially Joe. Lorena would say, "Wake up, Joe!" after every commercial break. By the end of the hour, she was having to yell it at him to keep him awake. "Wake up Joe!" became a lifetime family phrase. We used it to get a family member's attention when they were sleepy. Even saying it to myself right now makes me smile.

After dinner, I would beg all the adults to come into the living room to see my magic show or ventriloquism act. I was probably eleven or twelve at the time. Lorena was always impressed, or acted that way. Mom was usually there. Dad's attendance was sporadic and Joe had lots of questions and comments. I told him many times that a magician was never to repeat a trick, but he would convince me to redo a trick until he could figure out the secret.

This didn't take a great sense of deduction on his part because my tricks were quite simple. They were basically what I could find in the magazines we had at home, or maybe in a library book. Things changed the

Christmas I got my magic kit. I had requested it from the *Sears* catalog. For the first time, I had real tricks and real props. Joe was stumped by several of them and I was thrilled.

My success was short lived though. The kit only had a dozen or so tricks and after they had all been performed a few times, there was really nowhere to go but downhill. Finally, I had to retire my cape, and move to ventriloquism full time.

Joe and Lorena were kind of ahead of their time. They were the first people I knew that treated their pet like a child. It's completely common now, but back then, most of the pets in my neighborhood lived outside in a doghouse. Not Littlebit.

Littlebit had a wooden dog bed, with a mattress, surrounded by a tent frame. The frame was decorated like a circus tent and covered with red and white-striped side panels, and had a red fabric roof. White fringe bordered the edge of the roof fabric, and there was a little white pom-pom at the peak of the roof. At age seven or eight, I thought that was about the coolest thing I had ever seen. I used to help Lorena change the sheets on his bed when I visited. They were changed weekly as were the human bed sheets.

Littlebit was a chihuahua and he was not a particularly friendly dog. He was loving to them, but hateful to everyone else. As many times as I was there, he would still bark and yap at me every time I went in their house. But no one seemed to mind because everyone loved his owners so much. He was a smart dog though. They had worked with him a lot and had taught him to follow lots of commands and even how to read. They would hold up little flashcards that said things like "eat" and "read" and "door". Littlebit would run to his food bowl, or go stand and look at a newspaper, or run to the front door. It was impressive back in the sixties when people's dogs usually lived outside and could maybe fetch a ball.

When I stayed at their house, in the evening after dinner, if I was lucky, we would all load up in Joe's Chrysler and ride around town a while, and then stop at the Frosty Drive-In before we headed home. Joe would order three vanilla ice cream cones, and one scoop of vanilla in a cup for Littlebit. (I think it bugged Littlebit that he didn't get his ice cream in a cone like the rest of us, but he had not yet mastered holding a cone.) He would sit up in the back seat with me, and I would hold his cup as he ate his ice cream.

If I was really lucky and Mom and Dad went out of town, Lorena would move in with me, my sister, and my brother for a few days. Reno, as we called her, was a wonderful cook, a great storyteller, and loved to play cards. She taught me how to play double-solitaire, and I loved to play that with her when we were alone. When Mom and Dad went to Puerto Rico, she stayed with us a whole week. The day they were coming home, she came up with an idea to prank them. Since they would be arriving in the evening, after dark, she had us get some of Mom and Dad's clothes, and stuff them with pillows. We used our old Halloween masks to make heads and put them in their bed. Lorena made sure we had it all rigged up so that when they walked in their room and turned on the lights, it really looked like two zombies were sleeping in their bed. Just as Lorena had planned, Mom screamed and jumped, and it even scared Dad too. Lorena was laughing harder than any of us. She wasn't just our babysitter...she was our cohort.

When my parents went on another trip, I was old enough to stay at home by myself, but I stopped by and had dinner every night with Lorena and Joe. She even made her famous Reno burgers one night. Then, at the end of the week, she said she was going to clean out the refrigerator. She got a can of tomato juice and added all the leftovers from the fridge, including a couple of the uneaten burgers. There was corn and beans, peas and potatoes, and a few other remnants of the meals we had that week. By the time she seasoned and mixed it all up, we had a goulash that was just about the best thing I have ever eaten. In her small kitchen, with no counter space and a terrible layout, she still managed to make everything taste wonderful.

Lorena wasn't the only one that babysat. Joe was well known to all the families he worked for, and if he was painting or hanging wallpaper the homemakers usually took that as an opportunity to head out to do some shopping or errands alone. They all trusted Joe implicitly and would just leave the kids behind, knowing Joe would keep an eye on them. I remember when Joe was painting my new room in the basement, and Mom had gone out for groceries. I peppered Joe with about a thousand questions while he worked. Joe never showed any irritation and never acted too busy to answer. He usually could turn just about any question I asked into a funny joke, and I loved our conversations.

He was seeing three women (that we knew of) at that time. Mom and Dad would always laugh about how popular he was, and how the three women all knew about each other and still chose to date him. Joe loved to dance, and one of the three women was a good dancer, so he usually took her to the country club dances. Another woman was a widow with a young son. Looking back, I think that relationship filled a "family man" void Joe always had. Another woman (with the exact same first and last name as my mother) filled in the gaps in his social calendar. Everyone wondered why Joe had never married. We always thought that maybe he felt he needed to stay with Lorena and take care of her. Or maybe he just liked variety.

One day, Lorena was out of town and Joe was scheduled to golf with my dad. He didn't show up. There were phone calls to the house from Dad, and Mom was visibly upset. We found out later that Dad and the other members of his foursome had gone to his house and found Joe dead.

After the funeral, at the cemetery, I remember crying like I never had before. Partly because of Lorena sitting there alone, and partly because I knew how much I would miss him. Joe was only fifty-nine when he died in 1976. I was fourteen. We think it was a massive heart attack. I told my mom I had never seen one man being mourned by so many women. She said she hadn't either. We laughed about that for years.

Lorena began a heartbreaking decline after Joe died. Even though she was able to have cataract surgery that restored her vision, another bigger problem could not be solved: early onset dementia. By the time I was sixteen, she was already having lots of memory problems. She was still able to go to the grocery store, because I can remember picking her up and taking her there after I got my driver's license. But within a year or so, she was in the nursing home and not able to recognize any of us. I know this killed my mother, who still went to see her and did her laundry and anything else she could. I went a few times, but her not recognizing me was just so hard. Her illness had a somewhat rapid progression and, thankfully, she passed away peacefully. God, I loved those two people.

All through my life my thoughts have returned to Joe and Lorena. I have tried to understand how two people could remain as alive today in my memory as the day they left this earth. It's been forty years since Lorena died and forty-five for Joe, and I think of them so often...still. There are so many lessons to be learned from them. About cherishing friends, being grateful, living in the moment, and choosing to be happy. They had so little materially, but they focused on what was important.

I think of the joy they exuded every time I saw them, and the laughs they brought. I think of them never refusing to come into the living room after dinner and watch me do my magic show or ventriloquism act, no matter how tired they were and no matter how bad my act was. I think of the time they spent with me and how important I felt when I was with them. I have tried over and over to let them inspire me to enjoy every moment, every friendship and to make the best of whatever is given, but I know I fail miserably when compared to them.

At least I have their example to work toward. Right before Joe died, I had just graduated from the eighth grade. I think he gave me some money...I can't remember. But what I do remember is what he wrote to me in the card. In his typical fashion it was both funny and profound: "May the bird of paradise lay an egg in your hat."

THE BATHROOM PRO'S

I don't know what happened in Boonetown in the fifties and sixties, but every new house built, or bathroom remodeled, was gifted with pink ceramic tile. When I was looking for a house to redo, I cannot count the pink ceramic bathrooms I toured. It does not age well, and it does not go away quietly.

So, when I bought a little bungalow, I was not surprised to see that someone had redone the original 1920's bath in pink ceramic tile. When I began restoration on the house, since that bath was very small, I decided to add a larger bathroom rather than tear out all the pink tile.

I was meeting my contractor at home one day to go over some of the details. The man who was going to provide and install a jacuzzi tub was also stopping by to measure. Jacuzzi tubs were a very big deal at the time. Everybody had to have one... surrounded by marble and columns. Now they are mostly Roman dust bowls left in people's homes, a reminder of the return-to-elegance design style of the eighties. I had hired this guy from the Marble Emporium to install mine. It was just simulated marble, but my budget was sort of simulated too. I thought, ten minutes with them and then I could go get some dinner. I was hungry.

My contractor was a tough-looking guy in his fifties with messy hair and a good-sized gut. You could tell he had been muscular at one time, but things had shifted downward (as they tend to do). I can't remember his name, but that isn't really important. The other man coming to measure for the jacuzzi tub arrived while I was talking to the contractor. He also had a "former athlete" look about him. Kind of stocky with a gut, and looked like he had a lot of mileage on him. His name isn't important either.

What is important is that I was standing there in my newly framed-up bathroom, talking to the contractor and I couldn't help but notice that he and the tub guy were staring at one another. Intently. I thought it was odd, but I told myself I was imagining it.

I wasn't.

About that time the tub guy points at the contractor and says, "Hey, aren't you Crybaby Bobo?"

To which the tub guy replies, "Yes, I thought you looked familiar. Aren't you The Pretty Punk?"

"Man, how have you been?"

The conversation took off from there and left me in the dust.

Turns out they were both former pro wrestlers, and they had been in a few bouts together at the Florence Colosseum and some other area venues. They launched into a barrage of names that I would call pure comedy and yet they were totally serious.

One would ask if the other had heard anything from Bad Boy Billy, and he would say, "No, but I just saw The Toxic Tonic last week and he had to have knee replacement surgery."

"Oh no," Crybaby Bobo said, "is he doing ok? Last time I saw him in the ring, he tossed Big Foot Frank over the ropes and broke his back."

The Pretty Punk said, "Tell me about it, I was there that very night. Helped load him into the ambulance. He's never been the same since."

My head was spinning. Of all the contractors and tub suppliers in the world, two former pro wrestlers had to walk into my bathroom. Come on, what are the odds?

My brother would have eaten this up. He loved pro wrestling and watched it all through high school. I did not. In fact, I was pretty sure my brother still watched it with his boys. I thought it was all fake. It was more acting than anything. Well, very physical acting. I guessed everyone knew it was but sort of ignored that. Whatever it was, I was not enjoying this stroll down memory lane.

I was trying to get Crybaby (by this time I was on a first name basis) to measure for my tub so I could go get something to eat, but The Pretty Punk was having too much fun catching up.

I hated to completely step on their good time, but after hearing about The Big Dipper, Sean the Screw Driver, and King of the Jungle, I was ready for them to wrap it up. I didn't want to make them mad, but we were past the thirty-minute mark by this time.

The fact that I knew nothing about their profession didn't endear me to them. But I don't think they held it against me. I tried to show some interest, and even made an audible sigh of concern when The

Pretty Punk said that Jonah the Whale had advanced dementia, but I think it was obvious to them that I was not a wrestling fan.

When I got to the office the next day, I told my brother and a couple of the other guys about the encounter. One of the guys said I had to be making it up, just too much of a coincidence. I assured him that there was no way—in the whole wide world—that I could have made up that story. My brain did not generate thoughts about pro wrestlers.

The office guys were totally impressed. My brother immediately knew all the names I mentioned. He said I had some pretty big-name wrestlers in my bathroom.

The fact that the guys at work were impressed was a unique experience. My other stories never interested them.

For instance, earlier that year, I had gone to London for the first time and saw *Phantom of the Opera*. It had opened there a few years prior, and I was dying to see it. I was also dying to see London. I loved London and saw several other shows there as well. On the flight home, I was already planning a return trip.

After my London trip, I was in the office telling my co-workers all about it, and well…crickets. No interest. Then I mentioned that Don King (the famous boxing promoter) was on my flight, and they were suddenly full of questions. I said, "Yes, after the flight I walked into the airport restroom, and he walked up to the urinal right beside me." I knew it was him because his hair was sticking straight up like one of the characters in a cartoon that just set off the TNT, and I had heard the flight attendant talking about him on the plane. He was almost as tall as me. A giant guy. The hair added several more inches of height.

"What did he say?" they asked.

"Hello," I said. (You don't generally talk a lot to strangers at the urinal.)

They were still impressed. "And he was really as tall as you?"

"Almost," I said.

"You didn't ask him anything else?" they said.

"Like what?" I realized then that I might as well stop telling my co-workers about my trips. What was the point? We had so little in common.

After the "pro wrestler bathroom reunion" incident, I tried not to be around when Crybaby and The Pretty Punk were there at the same time.

Turns out it didn't matter anyway, I couldn't get a word in. They hardly noticed I was there. To them I was just another tall, skinny guy that probably played basketball, or some other so-called *real* sport.

Little did they know that I was really into theater. And isn't pro wrestling basically theater? So, the wrestlers and I really had a lot in common after all.

GREAT HEIGHTS

Growing up really tall in a small town is sort of like being famous without having done anything to deserve it. You know, like the Kardashians. I was very tall at an early age. By the fifth grade I was well over six-feet, and by the eighth grade I was six-foot-five inches tall. I was the center-back person in every school photo, and the tallest person in my school from the fifth grade until I graduated from High School. It was a small Catholic private grade school so that's not saying a whole lot, but even when I moved to a public high school with thirteen hundred students, I was still, at six-foot-six and a half, the tallest in the school.

I was the tallest altar boy at Holy Rosary Catholic Church and, naturally, the one that had to carry the big gold crucifix around the church at the Holy Thursday service. This took place every year during Easter week. The only thing I really minded about it was that I was the one that had to lead the procession, remember the music cues, and make all the turns. I had about fifty students following me around like little geese, singing hymns. I was always afraid that I was going to turn in the wrong direction or begin the procession too quickly and screw up. Looking back now, I wonder if they would have followed me if I had just kept walking one day, right out the door, over to the school for a snack.

One day we had been practicing our "processing" and singing, and I guess I hadn't had enough to eat. I had been known to faint on occasion, maybe because I was growing so fast my body wasn't adjusting. Anyway, the church was very stuffy that day and I proceeded to turn white, faint, and flatten a nun in the process. She was a small woman, who was trying to put out her arms to stop me. I could see the look of horror on her face as I was falling forward on her, but it was out of my control by that point. The next thing I remember was laying on a church pew with several people waving hymnals in my face trying to get me to wake up. I'm not sure how many processions I had to lead after that, but I'm sure they probably thought twice.

It goes without saying that the kids in grade school all noticed my extreme height advantage over them. They weren't mean about it or anything. Just called me The Giraffe, and things like that. I never really understood the giraffe comparison. Yes, they were tall, but they were all neck. I thought my neck was about average. I guess they were long-legged too, and that's where I assume the comparison came into play because I was very long-legged. In high school the names got much worse and not at all funny, but I won't get into that.

My mother had fits trying to keep me in long enough clothes, especially given the fact that I liked clothes a lot and really wanted to be in style. Unfortunately, it was the mid-seventies: platform shoes, bell-bottoms, and floral polyester shirts were the big things. Oh, did I mention I was skinny too? I was *really* skinny. Starvation skinny. You could see every bone. I don't think you could have put a much worse combination on a person as tall as me than bell bottoms that were a bit too short, and three-inch platform shoes. It was a horrific sight, but I was a slave to fashion.

When I was around thirteen or fourteen, I was in Wilson's clothing store one day and Charlie, the owner, and my mother were debating what might fit me. Of course, I wanted the new blue suede platform shoes with white heels, but she was dead against it. Charlie was trying to find some pants long enough for me that would not swallow me whole. My mother said (I'm sure in a loving way), "Don't you have anything that would make him look less emaciated?" We all kind of laughed but comments like that tend to stick around with you, for like, say, fifty years.

The real low point of my fashion life came in the late 1980's: *Miami Vice*. Two dark, tanned, muscular detectives in custom pastel linen suits with collarless shirts, lots of shoulder padding, and big flowing pleated pants. It was the hot trend. I tried, I really tried. But alas, white skin and pastel jackets do not mix. Nor do pleated flowing pants mix with long skinny legs like stilts. (If you take anything away from this, just remember, if you are thin, stick with fitted clothes. Baggy clothes do not make you look thicker, only the opposite.) I wish I could have risen above those fashion trends at that time, because the only people those clothes looked good on were the two stars of that show. But, unfortunately, I had to try. Those were some long days.

People thought I didn't eat, or had some kind of illness, but nothing was further from the truth. I ate huge amounts of food, seconds and thirds, as much as I wanted and never gained weight. Milkshakes, fast food, and all the bad stuff. I know there are so many people reading this that hate me right now. But it was pretty distressing for me at the time.

"Boy, doesn't your Mama feed you at home?"

"You're so skinny you only have one side!"

Ironically, often these comments came from folks with weight issues and big butts. Imagine if I would have said to them:

"Why thank you ma'am, for pointing out that I need to eat more and that I look sick. May I point out that you have obviously been eating far more than your share?"

My mother would have died. Well, maybe not, but she would always try to make me feel better, "Oh, they are just jealous," she would say. But I think she and I both knew they weren't.

When I was young, and so very self-conscious, the last thing I wanted was more attention. Everyone asked how tall I was. I was stopped everywhere. Sidewalks, delis, the mall, school, church, work, and grocery checkout lines seemed to be particularly appropriate places to inquire about my height. The follow-up question never varied: "Do you play basketball?"

At which point, gasps were uttered and mouths fell to chests when I said, "No I do not."

"Why aren't you on the basketball team? You are really letting down your school."

That one came directly from a coach, who incidentally had a gut so big he could hardly walk. And how was I letting my school down? I thought sports were supposed to be for fun. They would have been a nightmare for me. I was a klutz and awkward, and I wasn't about to expose my skinny, neon-white frame to the entire school in those skimpy basketball uniforms of the seventies. I can't even imagine the ridicule that would have followed. I was constantly taunted by the kids in my gym class for my long, skinny, white legs, not to mention the comments I would get at the swimming pool. Playing a sport I didn't like in front of a thousand or so people, who would expect me to be great given my height, shockingly didn't really sound appealing.

That coach could have said to me something like, "Would you like to try out for the basketball team? I would be happy to coach you and help you get started." Then I might have considered it. But starting out with a personal attack didn't really make playing a sport on his team sound even a little fun.

One of the comments I used to get from some people who thought they were really clever was, "Wow, you would really be tall if so much of you wasn't turned out in your feet." Yes, my feet are size fifteen, and yes, I know they are large but if I wore a size eight it would look ridiculous with my height. But thank you for pointing that out, and you are very funny.

I really wasn't aware of it back then, but this *extra-tall syndrome*, I'll call it, began at that stage of my life and has never ended. At six-foot-six, I am the tallest person in the room just about everywhere I go.

For a brief period of time in college, I did run into a couple of basketball players that were taller than me and it was really off-putting. Most of the boys on the team were the same height as me or shorter, but two were actually taller than me, one of which was six-foot-eleven. I was on the elevator with that tallest one a few times and it was really bizarre for me to be looking up at someone. I know most people look up at other people every day, all the time, but for me it was a first.

I'm not complaining about being tall. It's been quite a gift when I add up all the pros and cons. I've read that taller people get better jobs. If you are tall, you seldom need a ladder. You are noticed. You don't blend in. You always have a good view.

Well, not always.

I love theater. Live theater. Years ago I discovered that, for me, there was nothing else like it. I started going to New York once a year, but I soon realized I still couldn't see all the shows, so then I progressed to twice a year. The problem was, for as much as I loved theater (and I loved the architecture of the old Broadway theaters especially) the theater seats there were designed for people of an average height of about five-foot-eight and I was over six-foot-six. This could not only be unpleasant when it came to the seats, it could be painful.

I quickly learned to always sit on the aisle so that I could at least extend one leg out into the aisle a bit, but even then, it wasn't much relief. At many shows, even with an aisle seat, I would still have to sit for the full two and a half hours with my knees jammed so hard into the seat in front of me that I could not move my legs in any direction.

Another reason I always tried to get an aisle seat was because I hated to hear the moans when I sat down. Especially if the person behind me was short. I always felt terrible about it, but when I would take my seat there would invariably be this moan or whisper of distress from the person behind me. I knew I was blocking their view, and I knew that they had paid just as much for their seat as I had, but neither of us could do much about it. Knowing how much I love theater, I never wanted to ruin someone else's experience. I would try to scrunch down, but with no leg room that was pretty much impossible. So, I found that if I got a seat on the outside aisle, near the side wall of the theater, everyone would be looking at an angle toward the stage and the person behind me would not be looking right at the back of my head.

I also found I was more likely to get lucky and have a little extra room in these seats. So that was always my plan.

One night, I was checking out a new show. I had bought my outside aisle seat on the third row. But when I got to the theater, I realized my plan had completely backfired. Yes, I was in the seat on the outside of the row, but there was no aisle beside it. I was right next to the wall. There was a tiny bit of legroom, but I hate feeling closed in like that. Especially when you drink as much water as I do.

To make matters worse, not only was I on the far end of the aisle, but an entourage came in beside me: Dame Joan Collins, with her husband, and (I was thinking) some of their grandchildren. I had remembered her being made a Dame by the Queen at some point. I had not seen Joan Collins in person before, but it was hard to miss her. She was trying to act as if she didn't want to be noticed, but she was wearing a big sable hat, a full-length sable coat, and lots of jewelry.

Totally inconspicuous I thought.

I would often spot celebrities in the audience in NYC, but they usually did a little better job of blending in than Dame Joan did. Her husband sat next to me, and then she was on the other side of him. I was surprised at how tiny she was, but there was no doubt who she was. I had gotten a good look at her.

I had watched her on *Dynasty* back in the day as Alexis Carrington, and remember her well from all her fights with Linda Evans as Krystle Carrington. They would end up pulling each other's hair and wrestling with each other until they would both fall together into a fountain or swimming pool or something. It was pretty ridiculous, but it had made her quite famous in the eighties.

It was nearing intermission and, of course, I was feeling the urge to pee. I was hoping they all were too; but no, they all stayed put. So, I had to crawl all over them to get out to go to the restroom and then when I returned, they were all standing. I guess they were stretching their legs, and maybe Dame Joan got hot because she had shed her full-length fur and it had ended up draped over my seat. They were taking their seats and I was crawling my way back over all of them and trying not to step on anyone's feet. When I finally made it to my chair the Dame's damn coat was still there.

I was trying to gently remove it and hand it to the husband, but it was hung-up in the hinge, I suppose, and it would not budge. I tried to move the seat and continued to lightly pull and still it would not move. I was not about to spend an hour sitting on her sable, and if I had, I could just imagine me and Joan getting into one of the hair-pulling and slapping fights like she did on *Dynasty*. So, I pulled again and then pulled even harder, and finally got it out. Her husband was quite friendly, and I knew he was her husband because I checked on Wikipedia during intermission to see who she was currently married to.

The show turned out to be incredibly bad. I figured she must have known someone in the cast, or maybe her grandkids wanted to see it, because I could not imagine any other reason why she would be there. When the curtain came down, I was ready to get out of there, but, once again, the Dame and the entourage stayed put. I supposed they were waiting to go backstage as a professional courtesy to the cast. But I was stuck. I wasn't about to climb over Dame Joan yet again, so I just straddled the seat in front of me and made my own exit row.

I felt kind of bad for her. No one was rushing over

asking for her autograph. Even head-to-toe in sable, no one seemed to notice. Her fame was obviously nowhere near what it was in the 1980's, but as I walked down the aisle someone stopped to ask me how tall I was and I felt relieved. I still had my claim to fame.

I was in Washington, D.C. on a trip with a friend of mine, walking down a sidewalk near the national mall, and a woman with a group of children spotted me, and called me by name. Turned out they were with a student group from Boonetown. She had married my first cousin, I had briefly met her once, and she noticed me. I don't think she would have ever picked me out of the masses had it not been for my height. Same thing happened on a sidewalk in NYC. A bank teller from Boonetown called out my name on a very busy sidewalk. Had I been five-foot-eleven I am just sure I would have never caught her eye.

I could never rob a bank. Especially in Boonetown. Even if I put on four masks and a chicken suit as a disguise. The police would still be at my door in fifteen minutes.

A couple of years ago I was at the zoo with my niece. She loves animals and was studying all of them intently. When we stopped at the giraffe habitat I couldn't help but wonder, you know, if they noticed me. I mean, like them, I did stand a head above the crowd, and I had been called a giraffe all through grade school. I could feel their pain...people looking at them all day. Did it occur to them that we had something in common? I wondered. I think one of the really tall ones was staring at me.

I saw this episode of *20/20* several years ago where they studied women's attraction to men who were tall versus men who were short, and I was actually stunned by the results. At first the women were shown a group of men through a two-way mirror. Some tall, some short, but all basically attractive clean-cut men. Invariably, the women would all choose the taller men for potential dates. That didn't shock me so much until they started adding backstories to each man. They would tell the women that the taller man was, let's say, a construction worker, and the shorter man was an engineer. Almost all the women would still choose the taller man. Then they brought in another group of women and told them that the taller man was something like a garbage man, and the shorter man was a brain surgeon. Still, most all of the women chose to go out with the taller man. I was just blown away by this. The shorter man in the scenario was probably five-foot-six or five-foot-seven, and the taller guy was maybe six foot or six-foot-one. Was height really that important?

But then I also began to wonder at what point does the man get so tall that the women lose interest? Would they still prefer the man if he was seven foot tall? What is too tall? I'm just curious. I certainly would not want to be any taller than I am. It's hard enough now to find clothes that fit, and it is miserable to fit into airplane seats.

Now, at age fifty-eight, sometimes even a month will pass without my being asked how tall I am. I think the fact that I weigh more now and have filled out more has caused me to receive less attention than when I was younger and so thin. I kind of enjoy amusing folks with stories of bashing my head on this or that. Which happens often.

Recently, I was meeting someone at the front door of my building and I was rushing because it was cold out and was taking a shortcut through the parking garage. I was looking at my phone and suddenly felt my head rattle. I had hit my head on an open rear gate of an SUV. I've hit my head on *so* many things, *so* many times, I seldom think of it and seldom bleed. So I just put my hand on the spot and continued to the door. By the time I got there, blood was gushing from my forehead, down my face and pooling in my glasses. Let me just say this, when you greet someone at the door looking like a cast member from *The Walking Dead*, it really takes the edge off the evening.

Sometimes this whole "human sky-scraper" thing is just funny.

I'll never forget one day a few years ago when I walked into our local courthouse and saw a short middle-aged man looking at me. He was very short. Maybe four-foot-something. I cannot tell you how excited he got. I wondered if I knew him, but was sure I didn't. He began to tremble with excitement and his eyes lit up as he came running across the lobby toward me. By the time he got close, he was literally shaking and I wondered if he was a little off the beam. He looked up at me as if he were standing on the sidewalk in front of the Empire State building gazing up at its wonder. I could tell he thought he had something really funny to say. Maybe he had been waiting for years to use it? Grinning from ear to ear, and by this point his whole body vibrating with excitement, he said, "Is it raining up there?"

I thought, "Wow, that's a good one. Haven't heard that one...since lunch." But I didn't want to spoil his moment, so I said, "All clear up here, how is it for you?"

He said it was fine where he was, too, and left grinning and laughing. I was glad I could make his day.

Not too long ago I was at the deli having lunch, and this thirty-something, really tall man walked in. He had to duck to get through the door, so I knew he was taller than me, but I couldn't tell how tall. As he was getting his drink, I decided I needed a refill. Really, I just wanted to stand beside him and see if I could tell how tall he was. He dwarfed me. Wow, this never ever happens. Even if I meet a taller guy, it's usually only by an inch or two.

But he was a *lot* taller than me. Curiosity was killing me as I was standing there. I could only imagine, at his height, the number of times people asked him how tall he was. I felt real empathy for him, and even as I was thinking that I would never ask him how tall he was, I could feel the words forming in my mouth. Surely, I wasn't going to...

"How tall are you?"

Damn it, I did.

BEEF STEW

By the fourth time I entered Jo's Cafe, I guess I was considered a regular: Head Waitress yelled, "Ain't got no beef stew tonight!" across the restaurant at Maggie and I. We both expressed our extreme disappointment.

Head Waitress is late-thirties-ish, is disheveled-looking most of the time, and does all her ordering and questioning *out loud* so that everyone in the place can hear a person's selections. I call her Head Waitress because she seems to tell the other waiters and waitresses what to do, but I cannot say for sure that this is her official title. Maggie and I could, however, see that the husband of Head Waitress had done his due diligence that day: He made two pies, one chocolate and one coconut cream, both with about a six-inch-high meringue. Head Waitress had made her Thursday-night-only, turkey-size roasting pan full of old-fashioned banana pudding, complete with another six inches of meringue. I told Maggie this was reason enough to stay. She agreed.

Previously, on our first two visits to Jo's, no one told us about the beef stew. It seemed to be a well-kept secret. This one employee, who I refer to as Head of PR, usually makes the beef stew, but sometimes the one I call Cook makes the stew: two huge pots full that usually sell out in a couple of days. They only make it in cold weather, and it is not on the menu, and not on the specials board. You just have to know to ask for it. It's really good. Head of PR told us that he uses thirty pounds of roast beef per batch and I don't think that is an exaggeration because every bowl is full of huge chunks of beef. Really more beef than I even want, but I would never tell them.

Head of PR is also the one that circulates from table to table most nights chatting it up with the customers, and giving *nice* toys to every child that dines. Maggie and I don't understand this at all, given the low prices. There cannot be enough profit in a $3.50 bowl of beef stew for this kind of gift giving. But it never fails that Head of PR will come in from the outside storage building with a remote control car or a Barbie doll or something for each and every child eating there. We found out that he keeps a storage building out back, full of toys, and gives them to any children that come in, for his own enjoyment and at his own expense.

It just so happened that on our third visit to Jo's it was freezing outside. I just took a chance and asked if they happened to have any homemade soup. Head Waitress said they didn't have homemade soup, only canned Campbell's Chicken Noodle. However, she said, they had homemade beef stew that day. Well, OMG, that was just what I was hoping for. We both ordered a bowl, with cornbread on the side. Another server brought it to our table. We were stunned when they gave each of us a massive serving of stew, and I swear it was in a small mixing bowl. We ate until we were stuffed. Then another server brought us our dessert: banana pudding. The stew was $3.50 and the small banana pudding was $2.25.

Now here is another thing about Jo's that I don't understand. (Actually, I don't understand anything about Jo's Café.) They usually have about five servers working every night and you will get some form of service from each and every one. They do not use sections or stations or any such nonsense as that, it's just sort of "free-for-all" table service. It's not like one brings your drinks, and one takes your order, and one clears. It's just whoever passes by your table first. I eat out all the time. All. The. Time. And believe me, I have never seen this type of table service system in any other place. However, Head Waitress and Head of PR seem to be the only ones that are allowed to check you out…cash only.

We haven't been able to distinguish any formal uniform requirements for the staff but camouflage does seem to be required in some form or other, and tight jeans are always good. Head of PR consistently wears the same thing: jeans, a plaid shirt, his cowboy hat, and boots. This cowboy hat appears to be many years old. It's that old, straw-type cowboy hat, with many visible sweat rings where it meets his scalp. There is a rattlesnake-skin band that does help to hide some of the sweat stains, but I wonder if the snake might have caused some of them. I know I would be sweating if I had a real snakeskin wrapped around my forehead. Head of PR is really proud of this hat. Not only is the skin wrapped around the hat so that the tail with the rattles hangs off the back bill, but the head of the snake is positioned right in the front of the hat, resting on the front bill. It is poised with its mouth wide open in a striking pose. You get to take a really good look at this while he is checking you out… cash only. One night, I gave him a hundred-dollar bill, after asking if he had enough change. He proceeded to give me back change for a ten. I pointed out the mistake and he apologized.

I jokingly said, "Well, you can keep the ninety bucks if I can have that hat."

I thought he was going to have a stroke.

He replied that he would take that hat to his grave. Well, I was only joking but I am really thankful to know that, at least at some point in the future, this hat will be buried.

Jo's has been a staple for the working crowd for a good forty years or so.

For the longest time, Jo's was the place where everyone smoked. There was *no* non-smoking section. This is the reason I never ate there. But then the laws changed, and smoking was no longer allowed in any restaurant, so I decided to give them a shot.

The décor is pretty standard diner stuff: black and white floor tile, black booths, and the walls are covered in old license plates. They serve breakfast all day, so I figured the worse case scenario would be scrambled eggs. After a dozen or so visits, I've tried the hamburger and fries, an omelet, a salad (that one was a bad idea), the hamburger steak, and the stew. Trust me on this, the beef stew is by far the best thing on the menu, but it is not actually on the menu.

For the most part, Maggie and I feel somewhat out of place in Jo's. Not only do we not own or wear any camo, we don't own any football jerseys either, which makes us really stand out. Not that we didn't have a source for that type of apparel. You could throw a biscuit out the back door of Jo's and hit the Goodwill store.

Maggie and I were in that Goodwill once, shopping for something sequined and/or fur covered that I could use to make a friend of mine a Cher costume for a variety show (vintage Cher, not current Cher). So, I found this really ugly, beaded tunic that I was going to convert into a short-beaded jacket. As Maggie and I were discussing this at the checkout, the clerk asked us if we were local. We both said yes. She replied that she would have never guessed. She said we looked way too urban to be local. We were both delighted. I was just wearing my usual jeans and black loafers with some sort of sweater and a black jacket. Maggie was in something similar. I think the lack of plaid or camo was what really threw her off.

We have noted that many of the evening patrons at Jo's wear a good deal of stretch fabrics. We have also noted that if we continue to order the mixing bowl full of stew, and the large size banana pudding on Thursday nights, we will both be wearing stretch fabrics in the future.

I am going to have to quit calling Jo's in advance to see if they have the beef stew. One night I called and asked if they had stew. Head Waitress answered and said no, that Cook didn't make any that night. We decided not to go. I didn't know she recognized my voice. She did. So when we walked in the next time, she took a look at us and yelled loudly all the way across the restaurant at Cook, "Here is that man that called the other night and then *didn't* come eat when he found out *you* didn't cook any beef stew!"

Sorry, Cook, didn't mean to get you in trouble.

I have been back to Jo's a half a dozen or so more times since that last episode and it just gets more interesting. There's a new waitress that seems to be a rebel: so far, not a stitch of camo. She wears a different football jersey every night, but still keeps true to the dress code with very tight jeans. She also has a very interesting make up concept. She has plucked her eyebrows until they are non-existent, and has painted-in new ones in big arches about half-way up to her hairline. Then she fills in the large distance between the eyelid and the new eyebrow with a metallic shadow that compliments her jersey. She wears it with confidence.

These days, when Maggie and I walk in, either she or Head Waitress scream out, "Beef stew!" or "No beef stew!", depending on the availability for that particular evening. Usually, this is followed up by one of them yelling out what type of desserts are fresh that night. We haven't noticed them doing this for any other customers, so we feel very special.

We also now have become familiar with another cook that Head Waitress calls The Mexican. We weren't too comfortable with the name, but it turns out that The Mexican is married to Head Waitress, and she didn't stop to get our opinion. He makes the pies. He is also the one who usually gets the blame when there is no beef stew since he is the one that has to lay out the thirty-pounds of beef to thaw.

They are not shy at all about laying blame at Jo's. If something isn't done and done right, or is missing, they will call that person out, out loud, in front of all the customers.

We have also been let in on some secret info: The Mexican sometimes actually *makes* the stew. When Cook isn't there, or is too busy, The Mexican fills in.

Actually, I think his stew may be better, but I can never, ever say this because I would probably be banned from Jo's Cafe. Both Maggie and I feel that Head of PR is not at all beyond banning us. He is Jo's husband. Jo is a woman. At least that's what we have been told. We have never actually seen Jo. But we definitely think Head of PR would throw his weight around and have us banned if we complained about the lack of stew, or implied that The Mexican's stew is better. So we just smile and order something else if it isn't available.

There is a philosophy that some restaurants seem to go by: that all problems should remain hidden from customers and kept in the kitchen, which allows the customer to have a carefree dining experience. This is unknown at Jo's. Most evenings at Jo's, I usually am in on some sort of 'situation' amongst the staff, and find myself rooting for one of them.

The last time I went to Jo's, I did call in advance because I really was in the mood for stew and New Girl said they did indeed have some that night. This was after a string of about three visits, which yielded no stew. So, Maggie and I went. New Girl called me out immediately, in front of everyone, when I entered.

She had indeed recognized my voice on the phone and yelled out, "Here is the guy that called about the stew. Told you that was him," to the restaurant.

Before they even brought the stew, New Girl, Head Waitress, and Head of PR had stopped by to ask if we were going to have a large or small bowl of banana pudding afterwards. I said small, but Head of PR yelled out to everyone, "Bring him a large." I left barely able to walk.

I am sort of grateful that spring is here now, and they don't make stew in warm weather.

Who knows, maybe Maggie and I will stop by for a bowl of pudding or a piece of pie from time to time, but the beef stew situation was just getting to be a source of too much humiliation.

I think we will be taking the summer off.

TOM

Tom walked away from a good nine-to-five engineering job, a marriage in Little Rock, and returned home to Boonetown. I knew this because I had become good friends with his brother, Bill. Tom spent the rest of his life in Boonetown. For a while he was a sheep farmer, briefly a restaurateur, and then a writer, but he had his longest run as the curator of his very own museum.

The Daniel Boone Museum and Cultural Center was in the old bank building on the public square, a classic-style building that was now hiding in shame behind a tacky, yellow and brown sign. On the door was the only "Smoking" sign I have ever seen. Not "No Smoking" or "Smoke-Free". This sign simply said, "Smoking" and when you opened the door and your eyes began to water, you understood that smoking was encouraged.

At some point Tom had proclaimed himself Chief Resting Fox. No one in town really understood this announcement since Bill, his brother, said he didn't know of any Native American blood in their family. But Tom was sure of it and "became" a Cherokee Indian.

He had purchased the building and lived upstairs above the museum. During the day, he was both curator and tour guide at the museum.

On the sidewalk in front of the museum he had placed two outdoor displays, in some attempt, I suppose, to lure in guests. The displays were about the size of two card tables placed side by side, and were covered with two Martha Washington bedspreads. On the tables there were miniature models of teepees and log cabins, with little trails made of pebbles connecting them. (I assumed it was supposed to be some sort of model of a Cherokee village?) Here and there were some arrowheads—or just some rocks—that seemed totally out of place. There was also the occasional pine cone thrown in for good measure, and some left-over tinsel from Christmas-decorating attempts. The pine cones were probably appropriate accents, but the scale was all wrong. It really bothered me that the pine cones were at least double the size of the teepees. No one else seemed to notice, but I am big on things being to scale.

Lest you think these were just seasonal displays, they were not. They were there for at least five years. The only change was when he removed the torn and dirty, white-fringed, Martha Washington bedspreads and replaced them with Christmas wrapping paper covered in plastic. I supposed the plastic-covered paper would have been easier to clean—if anyone had ever bothered to do so. There was a thick, almost-fossilized coating of dirt over the entire display for most of its existence.

I would love to give you a report of the interior of the museum, but frankly, I was scared to go in.

I am allergic to cigarette smoke, and that alone would have put me in a full-on, month-long allergy arrest. Beyond that, I was really worried about what might crawl out of one of the hay bales or rock formations that were scattered throughout the place. I could see that much through the front doors. I was also turned-off by the raccoon skins stretched over some round, metal rings that hung in the windows. Not sure what the point was. I guess they did give some sort of rustic-woodsman flavor to the place.

One thing that I did see through the windows was his mother's needlepoint collection covering the entire back wall of the museum. She spent most of her life needle-pointing these large pictures of floral arrangements, and cats, and poodles in pink-and-blue color schemes. They were the favored decorating accents of the bridge clubs in the fifties and sixties and she had a house full. Tom said they were relevant to the history of the Cherokee Tribe since they were made by the mother of a Cherokee Indian...his mother.

Tom's father owned the old bus station, and they always had a restaurant there. It had closed when his father retired.

I know all about his father and the bus station because my dad's business used to receive freight on the afternoon bus. If we had freight, Tom's father would call our office around four p.m. or so and scream "FREIGHT!" as loud as he could, and then slam the phone down.

Tom decided at one point (I believe before he became a Cherokee) that he would return to the family's prior stint in the food-service business and reopen the bus station as a gourmet restaurant. I can't seem to recall the name. However, I do recall the dining experience.

Tom had bragged to everyone that this would be the best restaurant with the most extensive menu

Boonetown had ever seen. And he backed-up that statement with a most-ambitious menu. It was about four pages long and offered just about everything. Not only was he going to offer every Southern staple, he said he was also going to compete with four-star restaurants. He was offering everything from fried catfish to Beluga caviar. I feel absolutely certain it was the first time caviar had made it onto a menu in Boonetown.

Apparently, the staff of the four-star restaurants had not followed him into the kitchen to help with the cooking. It took forever to get served. A year or so after opening, the restaurant closed.

Later, when his brother was renting the building to another restaurant prospect, they found dozens of tins of caviar and other exotic goodies still in the basement rotting. Tom had walked away from the restaurant one day and never looked back.

After Tom left the restaurant behind, he decided to move to an island to live. He complained of chronic back trouble and thought island life would suit him fine. Of course, he had to take his little poodle Ceecee along. This poor little poodle was about a hundred years old, and rode on Tom's arm in the car so it could see out the window. It was a very small, white, curly-haired little thing, barely able to walk itself. Tom wasn't about to make Ceecee fly in a crate like other pets had to, so he got a wheelchair and had himself wheeled through the airport with Ceecee in his lap. He told the airport staff that Ceecee was his seeing-eye dog. So Tom was wheeled through the airport, wearing dark glasses, with his seeing-eye dog sitting in his lap. He had somehow convinced a local eye doctor to write a letter stating that he needed his seeing-eye dog with him at all times. (I don't know whether the dog's name was just ironic or if he had been thinking ahead all those years ago when he named him.) He made it to the island with the dog somehow, and managed to live there a while. But he was back in Tennessee within a year.

I believe that he married his second wife after he returned from the island, but I am not certain of the sequence. These details seem irrelevant, except for the fact that after that second divorce he moved into the woods behind his house, and lived in three, fifty-five gallon drums for a year or so. I think living in the drums was necessary though, because when he moved in with that second wife, he left behind the place he had previously been living in, which was the old family farm house. When he made that move (out of the farmhouse to be with his second wife at her house) he left the door to the farmhouse wide open, and the sheep took up residence inside for the winter. Upon returning, (after the second divorce) he found a pipe had burst and flooded the farmhouse. Being quite clever and an engineer, he found the lowest point of the old uneven floor and drilled a large hole to let all the water drain, so the sheep had a dry home. I suppose in a case like this the fifty-five gallon drums would be preferable to a house full of wet sheep; thus the move to the woods.

I have to give credit where credit is due: if this was a scheme, Tom played his part to the fullest. Not only did he open the museum, he also sponsored boy scout visits to his family farm where, according to Tom, there was an "Indian settlement". He wrote weekly columns in the *Boonetown Times* about his Indian heritage, and the history of the various Indian tribes in Boone County. He also began letting his hair grow long. It eventually got waist-length, and was set off nicely by his safari hat and Daniel-Boone-style fringed suede jacket. The highlight of the presentation had to be his reading glasses perched right on the tip of his nose, about to fall off at any moment. You could see him any day walking around the square, looking very focused on some business of the day. He was quite intellectual-sounding, and gave wonderful radio interviews about the museum where he came off sounding almost scholarly. Some folks speculated he was trying to get his family farm designated as an Indian reservation so he might build a casino there, but he certainly never mentioned it... and it definitely never came to pass.

He often wrote a column for the *Boonetown Times* called "News from the Museum", and it was great reading. One particular column talked about the museum's most recent acquisition.

Where it came from, he did not say. But, with great pride, he announced that the museum vault (formerly the bank vault) now held a prized dinosaur egg.

I was a bit skeptical.

But he went on to state that the egg had been taken to Boone General Hospital, our local hospital, x-rayed, and was verified as an actual dinosaur egg. I felt fairly sure the Smithsonian had some such scanning capabilities, but I was pretty sure Boone General did not. According to Tom, right here in Boonetown, a town of about 13,000 more or less, we had an x-ray machine that could not only expose broken bones and x-ray children's Halloween candy for razor blades, but could also determine actual prehistoric artifacts. I was wondering where the radiologist that read the dinosaur egg x-ray got his training, but Tom did not disclose this in the article.

Tom had spent years trying to get the Boonetown Tribe recognized by the state and to the shock of most local residents, he eventually did. It was a short-lived success though. Other recognized Native American Tribes took issue with the Boonetown Cherokee Tribe claim, and brought legal action. Apparently, Tom couldn't prove his ancestry or the validity of his tribe and was ordered to give up his title and close the museum. Tom retained the building, since he owned it. He also kept his mother's needlepoint and the dinosaur egg.

Not to be outdone, Tom then announced that he was part of the Native American Lost Tribes of Israel. And proclaimed that he was now Jewish.

I lost account of Tom after that. He had lost his museum and no longer wrote the weekly column. His radio gigs also dried up after his Tribe was unrecognized by the state. He still, occasionally, had an article or letter to the editor in the paper, but he kept a lower profile.

A few years after becoming a Jew, Tom passed away. I still don't know why I didn't attend the funeral. Bill's wife said a Rabbi, wearing sweatpants, arrived to perform the ceremony. He certainly had plenty of material to draw from in choosing his comments. Then she said some of Tom's friends performed various rituals.

At the end of the ceremony, an older man was asked to play Tom's favorite song. So, at that point the old fella went and got in his worn out Pontiac, and drove around to the lectern. He opened his car doors, popped in an eight-track tape, and proceeded to play a recording of Native American chants.

The old museum building has had a variety of tenants since Tom sold out. He left his half of the family farm to the East-End Community Club. It was located just down the road from the farm. Tom loved big dramatic gestures and he knew this one would create lots of drama for Bill long after Tom died.

When he was cleaning out things Tom had left in the farmhouse, Bill found boxes and boxes of books that had been printed and not yet distributed. Tom was the author. No one really knows how, where, or if any were sold, but there was quite an inventory remaining. I'm still pretty mad at Bill for throwing them all away and not saving any copies. The title alone was enough to sit me down for a Saturday afternoon read: *New York: The Whore of Cities*. But that masterpiece seems to be lost forever. I think Bill was still a little irritated with Tom about the farm and the East-End Community Club, so the books went in the trash.

A lot of people in Boonetown would say that Tom was crazy, but I never saw it that way. He was unconventional for sure, but Tom was one of the few people I knew that woke up every morning, did exactly what he wanted to do that day, and never worried about anyone else's opinion.

I have no idea who ended up with all the pink and blue needlepoint poodles, but I feel quite sure the dinosaur egg is on display at the National Museum of Natural History in DC. After all, it was verified.

HERE'S YOUR SIGN

Every morning on the way to work, I wave at Veronica. She's the tall, busty blonde holding the big cardboard sign in the shape of an arrow pointing you toward Extra-Fast Check Cashing. So many places have young attractive people twirling signs (usually in the shape of an arrow), around and around, to get your attention as you pass by at sixty miles per hour. Well, this is Veronica's job.

I guess she is doing the best she can, but really all she does is hold the sign one way, pointing toward the front door. There must be budget limitations at Extra-fast Check Cashing because Veronica is a mannequin, strapped to a two-wheel dolly.

She has long blonde hair and bangs and a surprisingly nice wardrobe. Considering she is not actually twirling the sign and isn't working up a sweat like the real sign twirlers do, I guess she can easily maintain her wardrobe. She has lots of sweaters and lots of leather pieces and a shocking number of boots. Fortunately for Veronica, they don't wheel her out during rainstorms or snow, so she doesn't need a raincoat or parka...but I am betting she has one. I would think it would be quite an effort to unstrap her from the dolly and change her outfit, but at Extra-Fast Check Cashing, they really give attention to the details.

I'm sure Veronica, being a mannequin, does cut down on payroll and workers' comp related expenses, but there are bound to be some issues with sudden gusts of wind. I've often wondered if they think that we, the general public, think Veronica is real, considering how much time they put into her wardrobe. Speaking for myself, I have caught on.

Around the corner from Veronica, over at the Daniel Boone Motel, I noticed another interesting sign. This one wasn't being held by anyone. It was one of those plastic signs, lit from inside, mounted under their main hotel sign. It has the slots where you put in the plastic letters and can change the message regularly.

This sign is relatively recent considering the age of the motel. It was just a few years ago that a man named Mr. Shaw bought the Daniel Boone Motel and installed the new sign and also tanning beds in some of the rooms. The tanning beds can be used by anyone; you don't have to be a guest. You just have to buy a package of minutes. They use the sign to promote any deals at the Motel for room discounts, or tanning specials, or whatever. They don't change it as often as Veronica changes outfits, though. Sadly, Mr. Shaw died not long ago. I didn't know this until I passed by recently and noticed the sign had been changed. I guess the staff paid tribute to Mr. Shaw in the best way they could...on his motel sign. The sign read, "IN HONOR OF MR. SHAW, 100 MINUTES FOR $25.00." I think he would have been pleased.

On the street behind my business, there are some houses. Apparently, there has been a dispute between two of the neighbors. One of the neighbors has taken a large piece of plywood, like a four-foot by eight-foot sheet of plywood, and painted it white. It wasn't brand new, it had some age to it, so maybe it had been used previously as a sign, but I can't say for sure. The neighbor was quite angry from the tone of the sign and, considering the lettering was done in red spray paint, I would say it had been done hastily. The sign-painter had put it on the edge of his property, and had spray-painted multiple red arrows pointing toward the house next door. I snapped a picture so I would be sure to remember it, and so you could read it exactly as he wrote it. It said:

"Russell Terry Brown, 401 First Ave, is a Theift who Pray's on the ELDERLY"

This was followed by more red arrows pointing next door. The sign has been there a couple of years now. Guess he's still mad.

The signs that are most prolific here in Boonetown are the church signs. It's almost become a friendly competition between churches at this point, one church trying to out-clever, out-pun, or out-shame the other churches. Competing to save the most souls through red plastic letters.

I suppose it got to be such a time-consuming thing (changing the lettering I mean) that a lot of the churches now have digital signs. This way they can really get out the message as efficiently as possible, and with visual aids. In my mind, I've sort of categorized the signs, you know, into levels of damnation.

Some of the messages are more focused on word-play, or have a seasonal feel, like:

"FALL LEAVES...JESUS STAYS"

"FALL INTO JESUS, HE IS TRULY UNBE-

LEAF-ABLE"

In the summer you can see sings like:

"GOD'S GARDEN, LETTUCE BE KIND, SQUASH GOSSIP, AND TURNIP FOR CHURCH"

I consider these messages to be more of the uplifting variety. Unfortunately, here in my town the uplifting messages are hard to find.

Then we have another category that I call Instructional Church Signs. These message writers apparently think there is still some hope for your eternal life, so they are giving you some helpful pointers for daily life.

"USE SONSCREEN TO PREVENT SINBURN," was so popular, I saw it at a number of churches.

"FRIENDS DON'T LET FRIENDS GO TO HELL" seems to just be good, solid advice. I passed this one every day for a month on the way to work.

It must have been the letter-changer at one of the churches without a digital sign who maybe got tired of climbing up the ladder with the letters, and just condensed that last message down to three words, "TURN OR BURN."

Then there are a lot of signs that comment on something Jesus has done or might do, like, "JESUS BEAT THE DEVIL WITH A BIG WOODEN STICK," and "JESUS... THE FIRST UNDERCOVER BOSS."

I find it especially interesting when they just put up a phrase and then attribute it to Jesus.

For instance,

"I KNOW WHAT YOU DID LAST WEEKEND...JESUS"

Or the more direct,

"I SAW THAT...JESUS"

Now I don't classify myself as a Bible scholar, but I'm pretty sure those quotes aren't in the Bible.

And some of those message writers who feel they can speak directly for Jesus can get very aggressive about it. This sign was up last summer at the church around the corner from my house: "DON'T MAKE ME COME BACK DOWN THERE...JESUS." Somehow that doesn't sound like Jesus to me.

But without a doubt, the most common theme among church signs here has to be the concept of burning in eternal flames. You can almost feel the heat.

"HELL HAS NO FIRE ESCAPES"

"STOP DROP AND ROLL WILL NOT WORK IN HELL"

"CHOOSE THE BREAD OF LIFE OR U R TOAST"

These have all been around a while, but I feel sure that since many of the churches have switched over to the new digital signs, we might see these re-posted with some nice, bold, fiery flames shooting up behind the message for extra emphasis. I really think that's what the original message writer intended when he wrote these messages, some nice hellish flames in the background.

I like how the person that comes up with these sign sayings seems confident that they apply to the reader. A sign like "IF YOU THINK IT'S HOT NOW... JUST WAIT" just screams to the reader, hey, I think you are going to Hell.

Occasionally, I see a sign that just doesn't make a lot of sense to me.

"IN CASE OF RAPTURE, LAST ONE IN THE SANCTUARY TURN OUT THE LIGHTS"

Is this really the time to be concerned with saving energy? I mean, you are leaving for eternity, right? Or does it mean we are all going to gather in the sanctuary and wait in the dark for Jesus? I need an explanation.

And, then there are signs that just don't seem to have a category but are just too good to omit.

"CONFESSION WITHOUT REPENTANCE IS JUST BRAGGING"

A real gem, I think. I always thought some of those churches that require their sinners to stand in front of church and confess their sins just wanted to hear the latest gossip, and maybe the ones confessing their sins were bragging a bit, so this sign seems right on point.

But, do we really think these signs are effective? I've often wondered how many spontaneous life-conversions have been caused by reading a church sign at forty-five miles per hour. Have they upped attendance? Maybe. Though I can't help but feel these signs trivialize organized religion.

Still, considering how many of these I see in a day, I must be in the minority. And even though they won't admit it, I really think it is a competition: once one church got a new digital sign, within a year, they all had one. You kind of wonder when, or if, this sign craze is going to end. Maybe someone will just have to come up with a sign that trumps all the others. I think I know what it will say:

"JESUS SAID OUR CHURCH SIGNS ARE BETTER THAN YOURS"

The Tin Man

In 1955, with thirty-five dollars in his pocket, my dad ventured into business. He had just returned home from the military, and was definitely the kind of person who liked to lead and not follow, so he dove in.

I remember going to the "tin shop" as we called it when I was five or six, and getting a Coke out of the vending machine for a dime. Sometimes Mom would leave me there when she needed to go somewhere unaccompanied by a five or six-year old. Back in those days, it was a small building on the west side of the highway. But by the time I made it to the fifth grade, he had bought the much larger building on the east side of the highway. It was originally a mule barn, but it had lots of space, and he continued to grow the business.

He had his own office now, and a bookkeeper, and an estimator. He was in the sheet metal and heating and air conditioning business. Some of his friends called him the "Tin Man". The business was not fancy, not even close. It was actually a huge mess, and it drove me nuts when I started working there after school at thirteen.

There was the front room, he called a "showroom", that was so full of boxes and junk and dirt and dust that you could hardly walk through. He had some gas logs on display in the show room. The dust was so thick on them it was hard to tell if it was the fake ash residue they sprayed on the logs at the factory, or just a half-inch-thick deep coating of dirt. It was the dirt.

His office was even dirtier. He, for some still-unknown reason, had wall-to-wall plush carpet installed, but didn't bother to invest in a vacuum cleaner or cleaning service. So by the time the carpet had been there a few months, it was dirty. By the time the carpet was there a few years, it was positively filthy. Walking across the room would cause dust clouds to puff up from the carpet and linger in the air a while. He didn't seem to notice, but my allergies did. And just about everyone that worked there, except Dad, smoked. So, between the dust clouds and the constant puffs of smoke, his office wasn't anywhere you would want to spend much time.

I don't think Dad started out with a business plan, but Dad had charisma. He was honest, did what he said he would do, and did good work, even if he wasn't exactly organized. Even though he had that reputation for doing good work, if you ever stopped by his office or shop, or saw the back lot, you would be hard-pressed to figure out how he could accomplish anything.

I remember one time when one of those aerial photographers came around selling photos they had taken of all the businesses in town. These pictures were large color photos, taken from a plane, of the roof of your building and parking lot and yard. I guess it was an interesting novelty since this was way before drones existed. Anyway, Dad proudly bought the photos of his property. Later, he was showing them to a salesman that had stopped by the office. The salesman innocently asked my dad if that was one of the aerial photos they had taken after the big tornado that hit Boonetown. Dad was in dismay and a little crushed. He thought his property was a sign of his success. But to the uninformed observer, it was just a big junkyard.

It drove me crazy that our company looked so unprofessional. When it came time to buy a new truck, Dad would just take whatever he got the best deal on. We had a fleet of blue and green and beige trucks. Some of them were two-tone brown pick-ups and some were two-tone green, and there was even one mustard-colored Dodge thrown in for good measure. Our fleet looked like a dirty rainbow.

One year when we got a new uniform service, I thought, "Finally we will have a more professional image." But that wasn't meant to be either. Dad just let each employee pick out their own uniforms. I asked him what the point of having uniforms was if they weren't *uniform*, but he didn't get my point. We had guys in tan shirts and brown pants, and guys in navy shirts and navy pants, and guys in light gray shirts and dark gray pants, and guys in light blue shirts and jeans. Then, of course, Dad made the whole uniform thing optional, so some guys just wore their own clothes to work. Every time I walked into the building, I just wanted to scream at the top of my lungs, "PICK A DAMN COLOR!"

Dad could not have cared less about clothes and had no fashion sense. He never seemed to notice his own clothes, even when his pants were two inches too short, or he had oil stains all over them from working on a piece of equipment. Had it not been for my mom keeping his clothes up to date, I can't imagine what he would have looked like.

But that didn't stop him from commenting on what other people wore or what they had done to their hair. He had a strong aversion to dyed hair and toupees, and talked about it a lot, too. If he saw someone with a bad dye job, he'd point it out. Sometimes directly to the person. And he would definitely point out a bad toupee. Hurt feelings be damned. The fact that he was bald had somehow qualified him to judge those with hair. If he had had a few drinks, he became even more free with his critiques.

I was always amazed at how much confidence he had. He certainly didn't need designer clothes or a nice office to help impress a client. He was comfortable in his own skin and people immediately felt at ease with him. He was quite outspoken, if the occasion called for it, and, often times, even if the occasion didn't call for it. The older he got the more outspoken he got. One of his favorite lines was, "You are exactly *wrong* and I'm going to tell you why."

Dad seemed to thrive in a state of disorganization. It drove me and my brother nuts. We were both neat-freaks and liked things in good order. But as far as he was concerned, things were just fine as they were, wherever they happened to land.

He pressed on and continued to expand the business. By the eighties, he had branched out into industrial construction, and had about a hundred employees. It was pretty amazing what he could do in his head. I called it "drive-by estimating." We could go look at a job and make a quick drive around the property, and he would have a number in his head by the time we got back to the office. Amazingly, he was usually right.

Working for industrial manufacturers became his

primary business. When he had to meet with executives from the larger companies, he always emphasized that he was just a "country-boy contractor." He knew these engineers and businessmen liked feeling smarter than a small-time local contractor with no formal education, so he told them how smart they were, and how he was just a simple guy trying to make a modest living. (Really he was impressed by well-educated men, and I think it bothered Dad that he wasn't educated. He didn't even finish high school.) But I always knew, when it came right down to it, he was usually the smartest person in the room. Often times, by the time the job was done, some of those well-educated engineers knew it too. He always earned their respect.

Don't let this paint him as a pushover. He was not. If he thought the executives from some big-city home office were too full of shit, or trying to make him feel like a local-yokel contractor, he would sit back in his chair, throw his pen down and toss out one of his old sayings: "Well, I'll tell you one thing boys, it takes a big hog to weigh a ton."

Think about it: it's true.

I called these his "baffle 'em with bullshit" sayings. It would always throw the others off their game a bit and, by the end of the meeting, Dad would have everyone eating out of his hand. I didn't get this gift, but he had it, in spades. People LOVED him. He was real, he had not one ounce of pretense, and it worked well for him.

Dad loved watching *The Lawrence Welk Show*...a lot. To the extreme. Whatever was happening at home was put on hold when Lawrence appeared on Saturday night. He loved the American music standards they performed on the show. We didn't know it back then, but as Dad moved into his forties, we discovered that he was a frustrated singer. When given the chance, he would sing anytime he could.

His singing ability was questionable at best, but it never stopped him. He joined the church choir. When the Kiwanis Club (of which he was an active member) formed a men's choir, he was one of the first to sign up. The choir, called the *Sharp-Notes*, was kind of a barbershop-style group and had about twelve or thirteen members. Some of the men had good voices and were musically trained. But most were like Dad: no training, just a desire to sing. It turned out to be quite a success. They would sing at all kinds of local events and provide entertainment for all the Kiwanis Club functions.

Over the years, various members of the *Sharp-Notes* were chosen to sing a solo, but Dad never was. I know he was secretly hoping for a featured role, but it never happened. At home, we all were pretty confident that Dad would not be offered any solos, considering that we often heard him singing around the house. And often we could pick him out when listening to the choir sing, and I don't think that's a good thing.

Then one year, as they were preparing for a Christmas concert, Dad finally got his golden moment. The choir director had chosen *The Twelve Days of Christmas* as one of their new numbers, and my dad had a solo. He couldn't wait to tell us all when he got home from practice that night. "I'm six geese a-laying," he boasted.

It took me a minute to figure out what he meant. But then I remembered the famous Christmas carol. I couldn't help but think he might have gotten that solo part by default—considering that there were only about twelve members—but he was still excited and took it very seriously. I would hear him practicing around the house, adding emphasis on the "six" at first, or then trying it with more emphasis on "geese." He was working hard to make his "six geese a-laying" special. And at least it was one of the lower numbers, so he got to repeat it several times. Dad never missed rehearsal, and his new solo made him even more dedicated. The first year they added *The Twelve Days of Christmas* to their repertoire, it was a huge hit with every audience. In just a couple of years it became their signature number.

As the years progressed, some of the members were encouraged to play around a little with their part and embellish or change a word or two to fit the audience, making it even more popular. Joey, one of the singers with a nice high tenor voice had been given the "five golden rings" part. Of course, this was a feature part of the song with more time to embellish and add flourishes, and Joey did. All of his added vocal touches got lots of applause and laughs from the audience.

I could tell Dad was jealous of Joey. Joey always got the good solo parts and was always a crowd pleaser. Dad knew he couldn't sing as well as Joey, and I could tell it got under his skin at times. Usually Dad would join the others in bragging about Joey's crowd-pleasing performances in the Christmas shows, but one day, after many years of Joey stealing the show during *The Twelve Days of Christmas*, Dad's bitterness finally did show through. I think it was Mom that finally said, "Well, why don't you just do more with your part?"

Dad looked exasperated, as if he had tried for years to do more with his part. "Well, Jooeeey got five-golden-rings, and you can do a lot with that, but you can't do SHIT with geese-a-laying."

Dad was never quite the same after my mother

81

passed away from ovarian cancer. She was his anchor. They had been married forty-eight years. They were kind of like oil and vinegar, very different, but when you blended them together it worked out. Mom had a quick dry wit and she often had to reel Dad in when his personality got too big for the room. This usually occurred simultaneously with his having too many drinks at a party.

By the time she died, he had stepped back from most of his responsibilities at work. But he still loved to have a drink after work with his best buddies. A habit that began when he opened his business, and continued until the day he died. Every day he would meet his friends for coffee at the coffee shop before the workday started, and then some of them would stop by the office at four as they were wrapping up the day. There were loud conversations, and there would be a big argument about something, and then a few minutes later they would all be laughing. Dad loved his friends and spent a lot of time with them. He truly enjoyed life.

One night, I think it was his birthday, (and it was after my mother had died) my brother and I, along with my brother's two sons, took Dad out the local steakhouse for dinner. Dad had enjoyed a couple of drinks before he left work and was feeling good, but not drunk by any means. I saw a man and woman walking toward us and it took me a moment, but then I recognized the woman. It dawned on me that the man was Dad's lawn guy, Donny. He was a really nice man who adored my dad. I'd never seen him without his hat on, so I didn't know he was bald. On this particular evening, Dad's lawn guy was sporting a full, dark-colored toupee. It was very obvious, too. My brother and I knew what was coming, and we sent the lawn guy all the subliminal messages we could. We were encouraging him with nods and hand gestures to get the hell out of there before Dad realized who he was. But the lawn guy was determined to get Dad's attention. We could tell Dad was struggling to figure out who he was. Finally Dad recognized Donny's voice, and the conversation that followed was really worse than we could have imagined.

Dad lowered his glasses and squinted, one eye shut, and looked hard at Donny through the other eye. "Donny, is that you?" Dad said.

Donny smiled and said, "Yes, it's me."

Then Dad went off. "What's that thing on your head?"

Donny said, "Oh, well...it's nothing, just...well..."

Dad said, "Is that a toupee? It looks like SHIT." Donny was stunned and began explaining, but Dad was not finished. "Good Lord, why would anyone would wear that? Looks like shit."

Donny said, "Well, I only wear it to church and special occasions."

Dad replied, "Well, that's good. I sure don't want you wearing that damn thing when you are mowing my yard. That's just embarrassing."

My nephews were literally crying at this point, trying not to laugh, or wet themselves. My brother and I were begging Donny to leave with our expressions and gestures, hoping to save some of his dignity. But Donny lowered his head and took his tongue-lashing like he somehow deserved it. I tried to change the subject, but it did not work. Dad was on his favorite soapbox and he continued.

He even addressed the wife: "Now why would you let him leave the house looking like that? There is nothing worse than a man in a damn wig."

Finally, after what seemed like an eternity, with more comments from Dad, sweet little Donny and his wife walked off. My brother and I were a bit tickled, to say the least, but we also laid into Dad hard about how horrible he had been. Dad didn't see it that way at all. He felt sure he had done Donny a favor. I always thought this was Dad's biggest flaw, that he always thought he was right about most everything. But he was so well-loved, he seemed to always get away with it.

Dad died suddenly of a massive heart attack at age seventy-four. He was on his way to the office. There was a large turn-out at the funeral home and my brother and sister and I greeted hundreds of sad visitors. He had so many friends and admirers. I cannot count how many men told me that day that my dad was the best friend they ever had.

And then Donny and his wife came in.

Donny was without his toupee, sporting only his bald head. I thought he had left his toupee off that day just to honor Dad's wishes, but no, I was wrong.

He said, "Remember that night at the restaurant, when your dad told me he didn't like my toupee?"

I said, "Oh yes, I do."

Donny said, "Well, your dad really did me a favor that night, because I never wore that toupee again."

Now the way I always saw it, if I had been Donny, after the way my dad had talked to him, I would have never cut his yard again. But no, Donny still loved him.

See, I told you, Dad had charisma.

Help Wanted?

My assistant Karen called me to the hall outside my office and said a man was waiting up front to see me. I had not made any appointments for the afternoon, so I thought it must be a salesman. He had told Karen that he knew me, and was sure I would want to see him. Again, I felt like it might be a trap: salesmen often say these sorts of things to try to get a foot in the door. But I was on the way out anyway, so I decided to see who it was, and see if I really knew him.

And, yes, it was a trap. But not the kind I was expecting.

He started off by reminding me how good of friends he and my dad were (I never remember my dad mentioning him). Then he indicated that he and I were pretty good buddies, too (I never remember seeing him before). I didn't bother to correct him because I had learned long ago that it was usually better to just let these situations unfold.

My dad had died a year or so before this, and that left my brother and I in charge of the family business. So, when the stranger began telling me that he had just left a very stressful job—in management—it occurred to me that he was looking for a job. We weren't looking to hire anyone at that time, especially in management.

I thought about stopping him right then, but he was really digging deep into his end of the conversation. I had a feeling that telling him, "No" would probably not deter him. So, once again, I decided to let it play out.

Keep in mind, we were standing in the front lobby of our building, and not in my office. Somewhere in his head, he had moved into a "job interview" situation, and pressed on with his promotional pitch.

He said he had been told we were looking for a manager, and he knew that he would be perfect for the job. He went on to tell me about a lot of experience he had in industrial maintenance. That would be useful to our company, I thought, IF we were looking for a manager.

I said, "I don't know where you heard that, but we are not looking for managers."

He acted very shocked and continued talking. He said, "Well, Tom over at Jones Welding said he heard you were looking, and was sure you would want to hire me."

I only vaguely knew of Tom and was pretty sure we had not asked him to do any head-hunting for us. I said, "Well, I don't know where Tom heard that, but he's incorrect."

The stranger replied as if he had not heard a word I said. "You know, I just left a very stressful job with my old company, and I will be honest, I never want to work that hard again."

I mused, "Oh really?"

He went on. "Things got really bad. The business

was bought by a company from China, and I had to deal with a lot of Chinese people. And I will just be honest with you, I am never doing that again."

I tried to sympathize him with, "That's happening a lot."

He said, "Yeah, then they started hiring Mexicans, and I didn't like working with them either. I'll just be honest with you, I really don't like working with people."

I said, "Well, 'working with people' is something you do run into a lot in management."

He said, "They wanted me to work long hours at times, and come in on weekends sometimes, too. Well, I'll just be honest with you, I might come in on Saturdays occasionally, but I'm never working on Sundays again. I'm looking to slow down, and not have to work so hard."

"Interesting."

I wish I had thought of a better response, something like the line from *Schitt's Creek* where David says to Moira, "I have never heard anyone say so many wrong things, one after another, consecutively, in a row." But I didn't have that great comeback at hand back then. And the stranger was not finished.

"Yeah," he said, in his final push for the position. "I am looking for a management job that will give me more flexibility, and where I can slow down, and take it a little easier. You know, not to have to deal with so many people, not have to work so hard."

I thought a minute. "Well, we do have the position you just described."

His face lit up.

I said, "But the position is filled. It's mine."

His excitement turned to dejection. I think he realized he had overplayed his hand.

Finally at a loss for words, he turned and left.

SHOES AND WEDDINGS

I love Chicago. One reason is the shopping. As far as I am concerned, New York is for theatre, Chicago is for shopping.

Around the time I turned forty, I noticed that, among other issues, my size-thirteen shoes were getting more and more uncomfortable. In Nashville, where I normally shopped, few places carried size thirteen shoes, and the size-thirteens I could find were usually the boring, blah, basic oxfords. I had begun thinking that they were making the shoes smaller, or that I was buying the wrong brands. Then I noticed that shoes I had worn for years were uncomfortable.

I asked the clerk at a good shoe store. He measured my foot and said, "Well, no wonder your shoes hurt. Your foot is a size fourteen and a half."

I began to argue with him. In the past, my foot had always measured just a bit over a size thirteen. He explained that some people's feet expand when the get around the forty age-bracket, and that it is not unusual to gain a size. He also went on to say that people with smaller feet might not notice this change so much, but on a larger foot it is more pronounced.

Well, shit.

I went in every store I could, asking for a size fourteen or fifteen shoe. Every clerk just looked at me as if I had asked for a box of plutonium.

"We don't carry anything above a thirteen", they would say. "Maybe we can order something?" No, damn it, I wanted to try them on now.

Thus began visits to bigshoes.com, largefeet.com and zappos.com. I mean I had to have shoes. Yes, they had the big sizes, but the shipping was outrageous for a pair of shoes the size of canoes. And I would have to order at least three times to get one pair that felt right. There had to be a better way.

So, it happened that I was in Chicago one summer, browsing in Nordstrom's department store. They were having a men's shoe sale...a big one.

I was immediately drawn over, and asked a clerk in a very low, almost embarrassed tone, if they had any size fourteens or fifteens. He pointed to the back wall and said they were on that rack. I then asked, "Which shelf?" assuming that there would be no more than one or two pairs in my size. A wave of euphoria overtook my body when he pointed back at the rack, smiled, and said, "That entire rack is size fourteen and fifteen."

There must have been a hundred pairs.

My heart began to race as I rushed over, still in disbelief. I had never seen more than two or three pairs of shoes in my size in one place—except my closet—and I was afraid I had heard wrong.

Could this really be true? Had I found the promised land of shoes?

I had. Italian leather, name brands, fifty-percent off. I had hit pay dirt. Struck gold. Found the mother lode. And I wasn't leaving until I tried on every, single pair.

I bought four pairs of shoes that afternoon. It was a good day. If I smoked, I would have needed a cigarette. How could I have not known about this?

Back in Boonetown, I was constantly showing people my new shoes. No one was impressed. "But they are size fifteen," I would say, "and I got them right off the shelf, in stock, half price." They would just give me a puzzled stare. Like finding shoes in your size was no big deal. Sure, maybe for you.

Then they would ask me crazy things like, "While you were there did you see a game at Wrigley Field?"

And I would say, "Of course not, Chicago has a Crate and Barrel, and a Room and Board furniture store. I didn't have time." They just didn't get it.

On my next trip to Chicago, I checked to see if any shoe sales were going on at Nordstrom's, but I was between events. I wasn't expecting to buy any shoes since I was still in pretty good shape from the last trip. But I had begun visiting Chicago about once a year and, since I missed the sale this time, I was pretty sure I would plan my next trip around the big shoe event.

But, as luck would have it, on this particular trip I found myself down on State Street, and I saw a sign for Nordstrom Rack across the street. What was this? I had discovered a Nordstrom's outlet, and once again I thought, HOW COULD I HAVE NOT KNOWN ABOUT THIS?

I rushed over, sniffing for the sweet smell of leather that led the way to a good shoe department. On the second floor I found it: shoe paradise.

Racks and racks of shoes, with hundreds in my size, at even bigger markdowns than at the Nordstrom's department store on Michigan Avenue.

And this was not some twice-a-year event. This was *every single day*.

I was light-headed.

Half of the second floor was the shoe department. It was massive. I tried on shoes for a couple of hours that day. Carefully narrowing down my selections to a couple of pair that I would take home. It was an experience I had never had in Boonetown, or Nashville, or even New York: shoe choices.

It still irritates me that the Cole Haan flagship store on Fifth Avenue in New York City doesn't have a single shoe in a size fourteen or fifteen, but Nordstrom Rack has all kinds of Cole Haan shoes in those sizes, just waiting for me...at sixty to seventy percent off. Note to self: Next trip to New York, walk into Cole Haan store on Fifth Avenue and flaunt shoes.

Finally, I had good shoes, and plenty of them.

On my next trip to Chicago, my friend Maggie had come along, and we decided to trek down to the Nordstrom Rack on our first day there, so that I could show her Nordstrom Rack and the shoe department.

Of course, Maggie had to have her picture made with every "freak" on the Magnificent Mile as we headed in that direction. I must confess that I do enjoy the occasional freak sighting. I took her picture with the Copper Cowboy, Billy the Rope-twirling Cowboy that juggles toilet plungers, and then with the Chicago Contortionist, who dresses in a lime green leotard and manages to squeeze his entire body through the head of a tennis racket without the strings. (That, I must say, was quite impressive. Look it up on YouTube.) He also compresses himself into a box not much larger than one of my shoeboxes. After taking her picture with a couple dressed as a wedding cake, we finally made it to State Street, and noticed a commotion at Filene's Basement.

Imagine our complete and utter surprise when we found we had walked right into the "Running of the Brides." It was right up our alley: a freak show of brides-to-be, complete with air conditioning.

I detest weddings. Loathe them. Maybe if I just had to attend them, I would feel differently, but I have had the bad-good fortune to be involved in more weddings than I care to remember. The sad thing is that what should be a joyful occasion is almost always NOT, because of the jealousy and manipulation of one or more members on one, or both, sides of the family.

The bride and groom get swept up in a tidal wave of activities that are too big, too close together, and too stressful. The families are right there with them, and even the best-intentioned family members begin to have frayed nerves and say things they should not.

I truly believe that the beginning of most "in-law issues" start during the planning and execution of the wedding. My friend Amy might be a case-in-point.

Amy's daughter and her fiancé decided to get married. They wanted to just run away to Gulf Shores and tie the knot. Amy was fine with that, and was already gassing up their car for the trip. But the groom's mother had a different plan. The groom's mom insisted they have a real wedding, so that she could attend and be involved. Of course, this meant that Amy, the mother-of-the-bride, had to plan and produce a wedding. Amy was not happy.

Amy called me, asking me to throw together some flowers for the event. One thing I was assured of, if Amy was in charge, it would not be stressful, so I agreed.

The bride and groom wanted to keep the event as

small and simple as possible, so they decided to have it in Amy's back yard, and put a couple of small tents up for the reception. There were tons of flowerbeds in her yard, so I instructed her to pick all the fresh blooms they could find that morning, and to get me some tall urns.

The flower arrangements came together well. I was pleased. I used the two huge urns of flowers to create a frame for the ceremony, and then made some arrangements for the food tables.

Time was quickly approaching for the bride and groom to walk down the garden path. Someone just happened to notice that the wedding cake had not arrived. I had been so busy working on the flowers, I had completely ignored all the food-related activities. But as soon as I walked into the kitchen, I met some distraught women.

Amy was pretty calm about the whole thing. She said was sure she had put down a deposit and confirmed the cake, but couldn't get the guy to answer his phone. I could tell she wasn't too worried about not having a wedding cake, but the other relatives of the bride and groom were. By now we were about fifteen minutes from when the ceremony was supposed to start. Amy looked at me and said, "Before these women completely flip out, go do something."

Considering that, among my friends, I am typically more closely associated with e-coli than gourmet cooking, I figured that Amy was expecting me to be creative...not bake a cake. As luck would have it, there was a Food World about five minutes away that I knew had a bakery.

I wasn't expecting them to have a wedding cake on hand, but I felt sure they would have some birthday cakes, and that would suffice. I loaded my cart with four really ugly white birthday cakes, with horrible blue and yellow roses. Thankfully, the cake icing was white. I secured them into the back seat and was off.

Back at the kitchen, I grabbed a knife and whacked off all the top layer of decorations leaving just the white icing. I stacked the round smaller cakes on the larger rectangular cakes and then found enough greenery and discarded flowers from my flower arrangements to make a cake-topper of roses. I managed to cover-up most of the seams where I had stacked the cakes. From the right angle it looked pretty good. I doubt Martha Stewart will have me as guest chef next season, but I managed to have the cake on the table by the time the ceremony was over, and there was a wedding cake to cut for pictures. Amy was delighted, and the story got big laughs at the reception.

I think that was the only wedding where I actually had fun.

I wasn't sure what to think about this "Running of the Brides" thing at Filene's. I had heard of it, yes. I just wasn't quite prepared for the actual event.

It had been featured on the *Today Show*, but it was quite different in person. It was obvious that these brides had been preparing for some time. I remember from the *Today Show* segment that Filene's Basement would bring in hundreds of high-end designer wedding gowns that would retail in the five to ten-thousand-dollar range, and sell them all for one price. As I recall it was $600.00. They were all end-of-season samples and were all one-of-a-kind. At that price, it created enormous excitement for the brides.

Looking around, you could see that all the brides had brought teams, and were well prepared for combat. It appeared the teams mostly consisted of the bridesmaids, grooms, and groomsmen. Some of the teams were dressed alike, some wore matching shirts and sweatbands, some teams wore matching head antennas with those bouncy balls on them, and some just wore their running clothes.

From what I saw on the *Today Show*, the brides and their teams would be lined up all around the block from the wee hours of the morning and rush the racks as soon as the doors were open. Then team members would grab all the dresses they could hold, and run with them to an established spot for their fittings. When a bride finally found her perfect dress her team would let out cheers, and bells and whistles would go off at the check register. It was a very friendly type of competition because all the teams cheered when another bride found *the* dress.

The actual "run" for the dresses had already occurred when we got there. All the brides had found a spot to strip down and try on the dresses. Women were everywhere, in their underwear or body suits or Spanx, with their teams holding the extra dresses, helping button buttons, and offering opinions. I found it really hard to hold back my opinions in a few cases. But then I thought, who am I to deny them a "what-was-I-thinking?" moment later in life. Team members would trade dresses back and forth with other teams to try to get the perfect one.

It was obvious that some girls were a bit shyer than others. Some girls were more covered and some were well-surrounded by their friends to give them privacy. But this one bride was down to her thong, standing out in the aisle, slipping on a dress in front of her friends. I thought maybe she wanted to show them her butt tattoo, or maybe she was just a spur-of-the-moment bride, and hadn't planned to try on dresses that day. Either way she was having fun. Personally, I had just about rather strip down in front of a store full of strangers than expose myself to a circle of my closest friends. She was a free spirit, and doing both.

As I looked around the room it became obvious to me that this was yet another case where we had been outsmarted by the Chinese: While all the other brides were standing out in the middle of the floor, encircled by their teams, and being told by one bridesmaid or the other how each dress looked on them, the Chinese bride didn't have to wonder. One of her team members had brought a floor-length mirror. His sole purpose was to stand there and hold the mirror for the bride to see herself. The screws were still hanging off the back where they had taken it off the wall. As they exited the store to the bells and whistles that sounded when a bride found her dress, the Chinese bride knew exactly how she looked in her dress. All the other brides just had to wonder.

Out on the sidewalk, they walked away, hauling the huge bag filled with the discounted designer gown. The mirror man followed behind, still holding the mirror as they all lined up at the bus stop, waiting for the Uptown 6.

I told Maggie that I could understand the excitement of the brides. The first time I discovered shelves of size fifteen shoes at Nordstrom Rack, I was thrilled. They didn't set off bells and whistles for me when I found my shoes, but I still get weak in the knees when I think about all those racks of shoes in MY size. Chicago just has that magic about it.

I hear they have ball games there, too.

Don Jackson, Loaded Gun

One Saturday night when I was about sixteen years old, I was home alone because my parents had gone over to a neighbor's house for dinner. They had a social life and I didn't, so I was watching some TV. The phone rang. It was Mrs. Jackson.

Well, most people called her Miss Beatrice. She was old south, bigger-than-life, with a big ol' southern drawl that made me sound almost northern. She still wore big wide-brimmed hats to church and drove a huge Lincoln Towne Car. She was my little-town version of a seventy-year-old Scarlett O'Hara. I liked Miss Beatrice a lot and she liked me. I guess that's why she felt comfortable on the phone with me.

She pronounced my name (Bob) with about ten letters rather than the usual three. This is how the conversation went.

"Baaawwwb, is your Faaawwther home?"

"No Miss Beatrice, he's out having dinner with friends," I said.

"Oh, well, I needed to taawwlk to him about Don. That son-of-a-bitch husband of mine has taken a gun, and said he's flying to California tonight and is going to find my brother-in-law and kill him."

I said something like, "Are you kidding?", but she seemed pretty serious. I offered to go and get my dad.

"Oh no, huuuuney, don't baawther him. We can taawwlk later."

"Trust me, Miss Beatrice, it won't bother him. I'm pretty sure he'll want to know about this. He's just next door, I'll go get him."

"Well, if you think it won't baawther him," she said.

I made a quick dash over next door. I didn't really care if it bothered Dad or not, I was wanting to hear the rest of this story. I also really didn't think it was a great idea to sit on this information while someone might be getting shot.

On the way there, I was trying to decide if I thought Don might really shoot someone. By the time I got there I was thinking it was at least a fifty-percent chance.

My mom and dad had dinner with the Johnsons, or vice versa, most Saturday nights, and they usually spent an hour or two talking afterwards. The Johnsons loved to have a good time and entertain, and seemed to always be able to cast aside any little issues of the day in order to have a drink or a chat with friends. Pearl Johnson was a full-figured woman in her early sixties. She was always very friendly to me too. Pearl and I always had a nice chat when I took vegetables over to her from my parents' garden.

One day when I was in college, I was making a delivery and Pearl answered the door.

"Mom sent some okra" I said. Pearl, always the hostess, asked me to come in for coffee. "No, no" I said, "I've obviously caught you at a bad time, I'll catch up another time."

"Oh no, come in and have some coffee, I'm not doing a thing." she said.

Once I again, I said I needed to go and, once

again, she insisted I stay.

I guess she finally noticed the look on my face and maybe then it dawned on her.

"Oh, I forgot, I'm just in my bra and panties, I can go put on a robe" she said.

"Oh no, I need to get back to work" I said as I made a quick exit. I always wished I could be as carefree as Pearl, but maybe a just a tad bit more self-aware.

But here I was now, bringing my dad news about the phone call with Miss Beatrice. Dad, like me, felt it was worth cutting their evening short. He and Mom came home, and Dad called Miss Beatrice.

She told him that, for some reason, Don had just flown into a rage about her new brother-in-law. Beatrice had a sister, named Lovey, who had been a widow for many years. That past summer, Lovey had met a man on a cruise and they had just gotten married. Beatrice was delighted for her, but Don was not. Don said there was no doubt that the man was after her money and was just using her.

The fact that this is exactly how Don got his money popped into my mind, but there wasn't time to get into that now.

Apparently, Beatrice told Don that the man was an Episcopal priest, and she doubted he had ulterior motives. But Don wasn't having it. He thought that since priests don't make much money, he had even more reason to go after Lovey's money. So, with these valid (in his mind) reasons, he threw a couple of guns in his suitcase and headed to the Nashville airport.

When I was young, I liked Don. But I didn't know him very well. Don was definitely eccentric and he stood out among Dad's friends. (And Dad had some very interesting friends, so this is saying something.)

Don always wore a big straw cowboy hat, a belt with a huge oval buckle, and cowboy boots. I never heard of him riding or owning a horse, but he looked the part. He had a fragile ego, needed constant praise, and talked a lot about being a brilliant business man. Dad said Don was divorced, and that he wasn't well-off when he came to town. Then he married Miss Beatrice, who had many assets. That fact seemed to have been long forgotten by Don.

My dad loved to remind Don that he had married well. It made Don furious. He would brag about all the money he made selling a prime piece of real estate (which Beatrice had, incidentally, inherited from her parents), or he would boast about how well he did in the farming business, which he, incidentally, took over from Beatrice's family.

Don would also host these big Derby Day parties every year at his fine home, which incidentally was Beatrice's homeplace, a homeplace that was, incidentally, filled with fine antiques, all inherited from Beatrice's parents. The beautiful old plantation-style home was out in the country on a big farm that Beatrice's family had row-cropped. Now they leased the property to other farmers, bringing in a healthy income. According to Don, all of this was due to his brilliant business mind, not Beatrice's birthright.

Even at sixteen, I knew that Don was in love with his sister-in-law, Lovey. He would get so excited every year about the Derby party because Lovey would come and stay two weeks and attend the party and act as a second hostess. He would stop by Dad's office and tell us what day Lovey would be arriving, smiling from ear to ear. Mom said that he would fawn over Lovey at the parties, too. Everyone seemed to know that Don was in love with Lovey—except Lovey and Beatrice.

Everyone always sort of tolerated Don. The more I got to know him, the less I liked him, but I couldn't really name any particular reason...until a few years later.

When I was twenty-one, I bought my first house. Beatrice knew that I liked antiques and old homes, and she was so excited that I was restoring an old house. She asked if I had a fireplace, and I said I did, so she told me she had some antique fire tools she wanted to give me.

I said, "Oh no, that's too much and not at all necessary," but she insisted that I stop by the house and pick them up. Again, I told her that was too much, but she would not take no for an answer.

A few days later, I stopped by her house to pick them up and Don answered the door. He acted shocked to see me and I told him that Beatrice had asked me to stop by and pick up a gift. But as it came out of my mouth, I realized it sounded like this was all my idea. I had not wanted to do this, but here I was. Don disappeared and I was left in the foyer to look at the gold foil wallpaper with hunt scenes in the design. I always liked that paper. They had a professional designer decorate the house and I was impressed with some of the touches. But gold foil wallpaper cannot overcome bad manners.

About this time, from the other room I hear an argument break out between Don and Beatrice. They were both loud talkers and I could hear every word. Apparently, Beatrice had not thought to tell Don she was giving me the fire tools, and Don was having a royal temper-tantrum. They were getting louder and louder. The fact that the tools were hers, from her family home, made him seem even more like a big, spoiled baby, but since that's what most of his friends called him on a regular basis, I guess it all fit.

He was actually chastising her for giving away "their" property without consulting him first. I think it all came down to the fact that he had not been consulted. He didn't give a crap about the fire tools. However, I was getting sicker and sicker by the moment, because I knew one of them was about to come back to the door and I would have to act like I didn't hear anything.

In a few minutes, a defeated Beatrice came to the door, looking mortified, carrying a big potted plant. I guess that's what she found on the way to the foyer after she learned she could not give me the fire tools. I didn't want to take it, or anything. But she was humiliated, and I tried to act as if nothing had happened. She made some reference to Don having promised the fire tools to someone else, but I know that's not what was said during the argument. It was incredibly upsetting to me and to her. I took the plant graciously and considered dumping the dirt in the seat of his pick-up truck as a left, but decided against it. From that day on I had no use for Don because of the way he treated Beatrice that day.

Beatrice wasn't a pushover by any means. She had been married a couple of times. She had shot one husband before meeting and marrying Don. So, I never really understood why she let Don tell her what to do. She didn't actually kill that one husband, just wounded him, but I think, dead or not, her shooting a previous husband should have given Don some pause when deciding not to let her give me the damn fire tools.

As I said, Don's ego was fragile. And his friends exploited it to the max. He used to meet my dad and a group of friends every morning for coffee before work. One morning, he came in wearing a new shirt with a distinctive palm print—very resort-wear-ish—

that he had gotten on a recent trip to Palm Beach. He was bragging about the shirt, how expensive it was, the fine men's shop he got it at and, of course, wanted everyone to take note and compliment it. He was in the wrong crowd for that.

This was the least fashion-conscious group of men you could find. None of them gave a hoot about the shirt, or what they wore themselves. But, as luck would have it, one of the other coffee drinkers was on a trip to Colorado and saw the same shirt in a nice men's shop at the lodge. He got a great idea.

He bought the identical shirt Don had worn. When he got home, he gave the shirt to my dad first. He was the *least* fashionable of all the men. Dad wore it the next morning, and Don's mouth dropped to the floor.

"Where did you get that shirt?" he said, mad as a wet hen.

"I got it down at Wilson's on the square. Charlie had them on sale for $19.95." Dad said.

"You did not!" Don said.

"I sure did!" Dad said.

Dad left to go to work, but on the way took the shirt by Wilson's store and dropped it off to Charlie. Charlie, who had previously agreed to the scheme, put the shirt on a mannequin in the store window with a $19.95 price tag.

Sure enough Don arrived later in the day at Wilson's Men's store asking how he could be selling that shirt for $19.95.

Charlie said, "That's all it's worth. You can get them anywhere for that."

Don told Charlie he had paid $95.00 for his at an exclusive men's store in Palm Beach.

Charlie said, "Wow, too bad. You really got taken on that."

Don's face turned red, he puffed up, packed up his bruised ego and left. But the guys weren't finished.

Over the next few weeks, each one of the men came to coffee wearing "the shirt" and told Don they had also gotten their shirt for $19.95 at Wilson's, rubbing salt more deeply into the wound. It was such a well executed prank, he never figured it out.

But the crisis at hand was no prank. Here we were, in Mom's kitchen, on the phone with Beatrice, trying to figure out if Don might really shoot his brother-in-law. Beatrice wasn't sure if Don was serious or just being dramatic. Dad called another one of Don's friends, asking him to come over to help figure out what they should do.

Harold, the friend, was quite an outspoken country fellow, without a lot of tact. He and Dad and Beatrice decided they should warn the priest first, just in case Don really was serious, so they called Lovey. Since Lovey and the priest had met on a cruise, they still lived in different cities. Lovey was understandably stunned by the news that her husband was in danger. She just could not understand.

"Why on earth would Don do such a thing?"

Harold, not one to mince words, said loudly, "He's in love with you Miss Lovey. Don't you know he's in love with you? He's jealous of your husband because he wants you himself."

Mom and Dad and I were shocked at Harold blurting all that out, right there on our kitchen phone, to Lovey. But, at the same time, I was thoroughly enjoying it. It was a lot better than *Dallas* (the hot TV show at that time) and all that "Who shot J.R.?" crap.

Miss Lovey tried to act as if it was a complete

surprise, but we couldn't help but think she had to have some idea.

After several phone calls it was determined that Lovey's husband, the priest, should be relocated to a friend's house until Don returned from California. I would have loved to have had my ears on that phone call from Lovey to her priest. "Hello Darling, welcome to my family, oh by the way my brother-in-law is on his way to kill you, aren't you glad we are married?"

My dad and Harold were convinced Don would not kill the priest, and Beatrice did not want to call the police. So, much to my dismay, the authorities were never notified. Everyone was on pins and needles when Don returned. Later Beatrice told Dad that Don had been able to describe the priest's home perfectly, so that proved he had been there. Don said that he wasn't home, but we already knew that.

Beatrice told Dad that after Don returned, he had become a crazy person. (Like that hadn't already been obvious. I guess it had just become obvious to her.) Apparently, Beatrice confronted Don about his feelings for Lovey, and there was a big fight. He also must have threatened Beatrice with physical harm because she told my mother that she was now sleeping with a loaded pistol under her pillow. We knew that she was fully capable of using it, too.

We speculated that after Lovey learned about Don's feelings for her, she might have called him and told him those feelings were not reciprocated and they never would be. Something like that must have happened, because he cut off all contact with Lovey and would not allow Beatrice to contact her either. The only time that Beatrice would be alone for the next months would be when Don dropped her off at the salon to have her hair done.

Thank God for those weekly appointments. The hair stylist became the local Mata Hari and would pass messages back and forth from my parents and other friends to Beatrice, and would let her call and talk to Lovey on the phone while she was having her hair done. She could still talk to other folks on the phone at home, but Don was always listening in and she could never speak freely.

Mother asked Beatrice one day at the salon if she was afraid of Don. Beatrice said that if he laid one hand on her she would shoot the son-of-a-bitch. Mom took that as a no. But it was incredibly sad to all of us that Beatrice was living that way.

This went on for a couple of years until the priest died, we think of natural causes, but the divide in the family would never heal. Lovey did return to the homeplace a few times to visit Beatrice, but tension was high.

Don still had the Derby parties, but no one wanted to attend. Some of the old group did still go, to support Beatrice, but Mom said the parties felt more like a wake. At the last party, Beatrice was becoming frail and Mom and Dad felt she would not live much longer. I'm not sure how old Beatrice was when she died but she was ten years older than Don, so I'm guessing she was about seventy-six.

Don was again single. Lovey was afraid to return to the homeplace to get any of the family heirlooms, so Don remained in the family home, and became more and more difficult to deal with.

He set out to find a girlfriend. His friends were shocked to find that he was dating women who were actually age-appropriate. (They all thought he might go after a young trophy wife.) He retained his pompous air as he would meet or hear about a prospective date, and then he would summon her to his home. I was shocked that anyone would subject themselves to this, but I suppose if you didn't know his history, he could come off as a somewhat-charming older man.

Somewhere into the dating process he summoned an acquaintance of mine to his house. She didn't know that I knew all the history of Don, and didn't mention it in advance. I would have not let her go. But she went, and later relayed the events of the date to me.

Don answers the door. My friend says, "Hello."

Don says, "Well, you aren't much to look at, but come on in."

My friend says, "You aren't either you old son-of-a-bitch," and leaves.

End of date.

Considering his personality, it took Don a while to find a steady girlfriend.

The coffee club continued to prank him: he'd get mad and quit coming for a while. Then he'd sell some more of the property he inherited from his wife. He would stop by the coffee club and brag about what a great business man he was.

Dad would say, "Thank God you married well."

Don would get mad, and the process would repeat.

To my knowledge no one ever asked him about the night he was going to kill Lovey's husband, and he never explained it. My dad stayed on the fence about whether or not Don would have really shot the priest. Mom and I debated it quite a few times over the years. I'm pretty sure if he had shot and killed the priest that night in California, he would have never done jail time. I think Beatrice would have shot the son-of-a-bitch when he got home. It's not like she hadn't had practice.

OH, SHIT

I've always heard that old saying, "The streets are paved with gold." I think it refers to the land of opportunity, but not so much in this case.

When I leave Boonetown, heading to Nashville for a day or two, I can't help but notice a golden hue along the side of the highway. I'd like to think it is real gold, but this is Boonetown after all, and alas, the golden hue is just dried shit. It's from the horses that pull the Amish buggies along the side of the highway. I guess the amount of gold on the road depends on the horse's diet that particular week, but it's pretty consistent, and when it dries out, you get some golden tones.

I see it, an almost-continuous trail of it, along the side of the road all the way from Boonetown to the Amish Country every time I drive north. It's all over town too. It's really inevitable I suppose: Wherever you see a buggy, there will be a reminder left behind. It's on the same streets where children ride their bicycles and people walk, but there are no fines for horse manure, just for littering.

Most of the stores in Boonetown (like those in the

wild west) have hitching posts. Kroger, Save-A-Lot and even Wal-mart all have one, and also a watering trough. They put these facilities way over in the corner of their parking lot. McDonalds even has a hitching post. It's out back by the drive-thru. I suppose keeping the shit in a smaller, confined area makes it more manageable. Other cities I have visited, like New York, or Savannah, also have horse and buggies on some of their streets, but they require leather bags that hang under the horses and catch the shit. Not Boonetown. Not even a Depends.

Samuel Hershberger was an Amish man that stopped by our shop a lot. He always parked his buggy right in front of our building and tied his horse to the nearby telephone pole. The horses never, ever failed to leave us a reminder that they had visited. Then I would have to carefully dodge the horse, and/ or the shit, when I went to get in my car at lunch. If I happened not to see the pile and stepped in it, I would have a lingering reminder with me all day. Maybe we should have taken a cue from McDonald's and installed a hitching post off to the side of our parking lot, but since the new four-lane came through, parking space was at a premium.

In those days, our sheet metal shop still carried the old-fashioned half-round gutters and stove pipe. Two things Amish houses were always outfitted with. Samuel must have installed a lot of the gutters for his neighbors, because he sure bought a lot of them from us. His wife would often come along. She might bring in her potato smasher (her terminology) to be repaired, or a pot that needed a handle replaced, but most of the time she just remained in the buggy.

One time they brought in what they called a molasses pan. I decided to go take a look. I had never seen one. I knew that they sold a lot of molasses and I kind of wondered how they made it. I was thinking it would be just a pan that they cooked the molasses in, but I was wrong. It was about the size of a foosball table, and looked like a maze on the inside. It was made out of stainless steel and there where these little dividers that guided the molasses through the pan from one end to the other. I supposed that maybe it was for thinning the mixture or removing lumps, but I really had no idea.

What I did note was that the contraption was coated with a nasty build-up of sugar and syrup and black/brown gunk in all the corners. I made an executive decision at that very moment that I would never be eating any of the molasses he sold.

I thought about some clients I had that lived in Nashville. They called me one day and told me they were on their way to Boonetown and wanted to take me to lunch. I said, "What brings you to town?"

They said they were making their quarterly trip to Boonetown to buy some molasses from the Amish. The wife said her family loved it and used it *in* and *on* a lot of things. I didn't have the heart to tell them what the molasses pan I had seen looked like, but then I thought maybe all the pans weren't as disgusting as that one. So, I asked if they bought their molasses from a man named Samuel, but they didn't know. They said they just stop when they see a buggy on the side of the road.

I thought about going into a full-blown explanation of why I would never eat it, but then I thought again. I supposed that if you are buying your groceries from a random stranger on the side of the road, your stomach is up for anything.

All of the Amish that patronized our business drove identical buggies. Samuel said one man built them all exactly the same and sold them. They were traditional two-seater buggies with a little bit of cargo space behind the wooden bench seat...the original SUVs I like to call them. You would see them hauling home groceries and supplies, and occasionally a mattress will be strapped to the roof. Samuel had eight or nine kids and I always wondered where he put them when they went somewhere as a family.

When I was a kid, my parents would drive us out into the country to see my grandparents. We would often see a big gathering at one of the Amish homes: a wedding or a church event, I suppose. From the backseat of the car, my brother, sister and I would often try to count the buggies, and we would wonder how in the world they tell their buggies apart. There were dozens and dozens of them, but with no license plates, and no other identifying features. Certainly no bumper stickers. They would all be parked out in a huge field where the beans might have just been harvested, without any lane numbers or parking space identifiers like we had seen at the airport. I was puzzled by it.

After I got to know Samuel, I would ask him a few questions occasionally. Samuel and I were an odd couple standing there in the sheet metal shop waiting for Larryalan, the shop guy, to bring out his gutters. Samuel in his straw hat, hand-sewn denim pants, dark blue cotton shirt, and vest, and me in my on-trend late-eighties finest: Ralph Lauren red, yellow, and green madras plaid shirt, and some matching green chino pants. While, at the time, I wondered about his clothing choices, (he had to be burning up in the summer), I am sure he wondered about mine.

I asked Samuel how they identified their buggies at those big events and he would just smile and say, "We have our ways." I kidded with him a little, and asked if he counted paces from the nearest tree or pond, or if Cora, his wife, left a trail of molasses, but he would never reveal the secret.

Over the years, we quit carrying half-round gutter, and closed our sheet metal shop. We had long since quit doing any residential work, and keeping a shop open to the public made no sense. I haven't seen Samuel in several years.

Sometimes I wish I was more curious. I had many opportunities to ask Samuel about a lot of things. I never asked him, for example, what the purpose of a molasses pan actually was, or how it was used, even though we had built many of them in our shop. The more burning question I wanted to ask was if he felt, maybe, just a little bit guilty after his horse left a big pile of shit in our parking lot. Considering that even Boonetown has a Pooper Scooper Law requiring you to pick up after your dog, you would think that it might cross his mind. But he certainly never seemed to show any sign of remorse.

The curiosity thing has always been a problem for me, I think. I always seem to wish I had learned more when I had the chance, asked more questions. I do observe. And I learn a lot that way. But I think a lot of times I just prefer to put my own back-story with the visual rather than actually investigate. I must admit, this trait has gotten me into a lot of trouble over the years. So, I do, occasionally wonder what Samuel is up too. If he is still in the molasses business, and things like that. But I have to be honest. I sure don't miss the shit.

I know that while I find shit annoying, some people see it as an opportunity.

My dad's best friend of fifty years was a very tall, kind, funny man named Hank. When I was in high school, Hank went into the septic tank cleaning business. Hank bought a truck with a big tank on the back. He went to people's homes in rural areas that were not on the city sewer service and pumped the shit out of their septic tanks.

A lot of people made fun of Hank for taking on such an unsavory profession. They would make comments about how bad the septic tanks must smell, but Hank would just sit back with a big grin on his face and say, "Well boys, it just smells like money to me."

Even after decades in the business, Hank would still get a twinkle in his eye when his cell phone rang and he had to go clean out a tank. It was like every tank he cleaned was the very first one. He would always say that people were so happy to see him, and glad to pay his fee since their toilets were out of commission and often backing up sewage into their house.

Once though, he cleaned a lot of tanks for the large prison over in west Tennessee, and they told him they would mail a check. Hank preferred to be paid in cash on the spot. He called several times and still no check. Weeks turned to months and Hank was getting frustrated. He finally called the secretary one last time and told her if he didn't get paid that week, he would drive his truck back over to her office and return their merchandise. He got his check the next week.

Hank called his truck the Honey Wagon and had lots of slogans over the years. The slogan that was painted on the back of his tank had a hand of playing cards fanned out, and below them it said, "A flush always beats a full house." When he traded in that truck he was flirting with changing to a new slogan. One consideration was, "You sling it, I haul it." I always liked that one.

Hank always seemed to be in a good mood. Observing him all those years, doing a job that most people would think was beneath them, I learned one thing that has always stuck with me. In any situation or job, *attitude is everything*.

This would be a great year for a better attitude. It is the year of COVID-19, a very shitty year indeed. COVID-19 is still out of control, and people are still dying every day.

Because of the very shitty presidential election, I quit watching network television and went exclusively to streaming. I also started following Leslie Jordan on Instagram. I just love the fact that he always opened up every video with his trademark phrase, "Well shit, how are y'all doing?"

Before the COVID shutdown, I watched very little television. Maybe an occasional true-crime story, or documentary on Netflix. I had long since given up on new shows since I could never connect with the sitcoms being produced. It was like they were trying too hard, or were too silly, or just plain stupid. I grew up watching shows like *The Andy Griffith Show* and *The Mary Tyler Moore Show* and then fell in love with *Designing Women* and *The Golden Girls* in my twenties. These were great shows filled with well-developed characters. I had resigned myself to the fact that I would just have to get by on old reruns, since nothing new appealed to me.

But, as if to defy the logic of this year, I found a new show that gave me everything I was looking for and more: Totally original characters that were both likable and unlikable, characters that evolved, relationships that felt real, and story lines that warmed my heart. I never thought I would find a show in such a shitty year that would become my all-time favorite. But I did. With all the stay-at-home time this year, I find myself re-watching the episodes over and over. And it's really appropriate that, in this most shitty year, this new favorite show is called *Schitt's Creek*.

Here's to a new year. I'm hoping it's a lot less shitty.

The Letter

About twenty years ago, I decided to expand my horizons a bit and get a place in Nashville. I mean Boonetown had a lot to offer, and I still had to be there during the week for work, but I guess some people can't ever be pleased and I wanted more.

I found a condo for sale in a high-rise near Vanderbilt campus and I thought that might be a fun location for weekend get-aways. I wanted a place in a part of town that was very walkable, with lots of restaurants nearby (I still hate to cook), and this seemed to meet those qualifications.

When I walked through the unit that was for sale, I was very disappointed. The skyline view I was hoping for turned out to be a view of the parking lot and a stucco wall. I turned it down. But as luck would have it, I ran into a real estate agent in the lobby who had just put another unit on the market. It was on the sixth floor and, even though we had not set up a showing, the owner offered to let me in.

The first thing I noticed was that it did have a fantastic view of the downtown Nashville skyline. That pretty much had me sold on the spot. The condo was only 550 square feet. Basically, two medium sized rooms, a kitchenette, and a bathroom. It was plenty of space for me to use on weekends. The view inside, however, was not so hot.

The owner of the unit was a collector. A collector of very large things.

She introduced herself to me as "Jeanette without the 'e'." (I had no idea which "e" I was supposed to leave out since most spellings of Jeanette involved more than one "e", but I was already placing furniture in my mind so I really didn't care about the name thing.) She was very proud of the fact that she had paid nine hundred dollars to have a central vacuum system installed in the only closet. It took up half of the closet, which wasn't big to start with, and the fifty feet of hose took up the rest. Why anyone would need a central vacuum in a two-room condo was just another mystery to go along with the "e" that wasn't supposed to be in her name. There was literally enough hose to go out across the hall and vacuum the neighbors' condos.

Jeanette had two large, roll-top desks, a couple of dressers, another plain desk, a queen bed, a sofa, and a couple of chairs, all crammed into this very small condo.

While I could see the Nashville skyline view when I walked in, a shorter person might not have been able to see it over the huge chest of drawers sitting in front of the windows.

I was puzzled at all this furniture and the complete lack of sense it made. But I had already fallen in love with the place.

Jeanette said she had decided to move into her RV full-time, and travel. (It probably had more room than this condo.) I figured maybe she was going to travel the country selling roll-top desks.

120

After she had moved out, I was relieved to find that the place had a more spacious feel than I expected. The first thing I did was rip out the central vacuum and regain my closet. I loved fixing up that little condo.

While living there, I met a guy down the hall named David and we became good friends. He had moved to Nashville for work and didn't know a lot of people there. We started grabbing meals together when I was in town.

David had lived in New York City for ten years before moving to Nashville. But when he found out where I was from, and where Boonetown was, his face lit up. He immediately wanted to know if Boonetown was anywhere near Putmanwood.

I said, "Well, yes, maybe about ten miles away. It's in Boone County."

David was delighted. Then he asked if I knew a man named Richard Don Jones.

I said, "No, but that name does sound familiar."

David went on to tell me that this man, Richard Don Jones, was from Putmanwood. Then David told me the story of how he knew the name.

It seems that David was working as an accountant at CBS in New York when there had been quite a stir in the office. He kept hearing roars of laughter coming from various offices down the hall, then someone would run to the copy machine, make a copy of a sheet of paper, and hand it off to another person. Then a group would gather as someone read it aloud. They would be bent over at the waist with laughter, then gasping in shock at the content. Finally, it reached David's group.

It was a letter, from Richard Don Jones addressed to the President of NBC, and when he read it, he, too, was overcome with laughter. He couldn't believe what he was reading.

Even after all these years, David still kept a copy of the letter. If he felt down, he would get it out and read it to himself, and still laugh until he cried.

David pulled out a copy of the old letter, and read it to me.

He could only get out a sentence or two at a time, because we would both have to stop and laugh. We laughed out loud at the crazy foul images Richard had conveyed. By the time David finished the letter, we were both laughing so much tears were rolling down our faces. We looked like we had been crying for hours.

Most of the time when people tell me something is really funny, I am disappointed. Not this time.

David was so excited that I might be able to put him in contact with Richard Don Jones. He wanted to tell him that his letter had literally shut down three floors of CBS news in New York City, as well as NBC news, and probably ABC too. This happened back before cell phones and e-mail, and there were only three television channels at that time, ABC, NBC and CBS. There were no news channels and no Fox, just the three original networks.

The letter had arrived by snail mail, addressed to the president of NBC. I can only imagine all the hands it would have had to go through to actually make it all the way to the President, but it did. There must have been screeners and departments that looked at all the complaint letters, and filed them here or there, but this one was special. It continued to make its unlikely way from the mail room all the way to the top man. It caused an uproar. Everyone who read it was making copies and sending it to friends in other departments, or to other buildings in New York via fax machine.

That's how it hopped from the NBC offices over to CBS where David worked. All the water cooler talk started with one question. "Have you read *the letter*?" For the rest of the day there were laughs and jokes about the letter. Very little work got done. Richard Don Jones had done what seemed impossible. He shut down all of the major television networks for the day.

It's not that the letter was that earth-shaking.

Richard Don was simply very upset about the fact that every night his regular programming was being interrupted by the Iran Contra Hearings.

For those of you too young to understand this, let me explain. Since there was no C-SPAN, CNN, MSNBC or FOX news, any important news coverage would preempt regular weeknight programming. The networks would "bump" those sitcoms and dramas to the middle of the night. And there was no streaming back then, so if you missed your show when it aired, you were completely out of luck. So, Richard Don was having to stay up to all hours to watch his favorite shows and he was mad. Mad!

It wasn't just that the letter was filled with expletives, it was. But it was his creative use of those four-letter words that set him apart. I had heard all of the words in the letter many times (and used most of them myself) but never, ever, in the way he used them.

The fact that the letter was handprinted on personalized stationery just made it more impactful. Richard Don's ability to string together a group of foul words to paint a picture was simply unparalleled.

It's a real shame that I cannot quote much from the letter, but a few phrases do come to mind. He wasn't a fan of President Reagan, calling him a "fog-brained old bastard maggot of a president."

And he was quite unhappy with the president of the network, calling him a "#$*! weasel-headed son of a flop-eared bitch."

But I think asking the network president to "go and suck a septic tank dry with a straw" created the most memorable mental image.

He also used "boils and carbuncles" to great effect, more than once, in combination with, well, never mind. I can't say that. Then, he ended the letter with another, very well-described image, this one of the network president trapped in "a mosquito infested swamp after a plane crash had broken every bone in his body." Of course, this is the edited version.

I would love to print a copy of the letter here for you to read, but I simply can't. It's too much. Too offensive and too filthy. I can tell you that when a man from Putmanwood, Tennessee can out-cuss and out-insult a group of hardened New York newsmen and women, who are in the toughest business and in the toughest city, he has done something.

Still, I don't think the letter actually achieved his goal. The networks continued to preempt programming for big news stories.

I do have to say it did give me some sense of hometown pride, you know, knowing that one of our own was able to get the attention of so many of the top television executives. And to this day, I still wonder if Richard Don got a reply.

My friend David was dying to knock on Richard Don's door and hand him a copy of the letter and tell him that he was returning it to the sender, and share with him the story of how many people had laughed and laughed while reading it. I told David that Richard Don might not have intended laughs and could be offended by this news. David felt sure he would love to know what a commotion he had caused in New York.

I did some research and found that Richard Don Jones was no longer alive. David was pretty crushed. Not only did David want to tell him the story, he had also really hoped to see some of Richard Don's other writings.

David's eyes glistened with the prospect. "Can you just image" he mused. "Maybe he kept a diary. I'd give anything to read it. Surely they kept his belongings."

I told him I would try to find out. But I only hit dead ends. David was deflated. Alas, it was not meant to be: none of Richard Don's writings could be found.

I guess Richard Don Jones will have to go down in history as yet another one-hit-wonder.

ALFIE'S LUNCH BOX

I guess it's been close to twenty years ago when several new mysterious women entered my lunchtime world.

A woman had come in to Alfie's Lunch Box with Mr. Feldman every day this particular week and she seemed chummy with him. My friend Maggie stopped by my table at Alfie's and asked if I knew this woman who was eating lunch with Mr. Feldman. I didn't. Maggie and I were both regulars there, and we felt sure that neither of us had ever seen this woman before. We couldn't figure out where Mr. Feldman's wife was either.

The Feldmans moved to town from upstate New York earlier that year. They stayed pretty much to themselves, but they usually came into Alfie's together. Everyone considered them regulars. I certainly saw them there just about every time I went in, which was pretty often: I ate at Alfie's almost every day.

Alfie, the owner, was an older woman who had retired from a state job. I had known Alfie all my life, and she had to be the hardest-working woman I had ever known. That's saying a lot. I knew a lot of hard-working women, especially my mother. Alfie had six children and had raised them alone. She was the cook at the Catholic school cafeteria when I was in grade school.

The other kids at Holy Rosary thought the two cafeteria ladies were cranky, but I didn't mind, the food was too good to care. Alfie was a distant cousin of mine, and she was an amazing cook. Kids in my neighborhood who attended public schools, were complaining about what they had to eat in the cafeteria, while I was perfectly happy to enjoy the fried chicken, deep-dish pizza, and mile high tuna salad sandwiches we had at Holy Rosary. This would be followed by the best peach and apple cobbler you could find and, on lucky days, these super-huge, thick, cinnamon rolls that would melt in your mouth. Our school didn't get any supplements from the government, so they were free to serve whatever they wanted...and it was fantastic.

Alfie was very slim. I suppose because she worked so fast and so hard, a calorie would never be able to catch her. And when we went through the cafeteria line, she sort of assessed your caloric needs by your appearance. I was super tall and super skinny, so she always loaded up my tray with a heavy hand and sometimes would even give me two cinnamon rolls. Days like that were very good indeed.

After I went to high school and later on to college, I really missed her food. I realized no school cafeteria anywhere could come close to what I had grown up with.

I graduated from grade school and I would still see her in church on Sunday mornings. I thought I had done well to get to the 8:00 a.m. service on time. But she would always tell me, on the way out of church, all the chores she had completed before she came to church. Just from listening to her I would be completely exhausted by the time we got to the door. Then she would walk briskly to her car and blast off home to tackle more chores. No wonder she looked a little disheveled by the time she rushed into her pew right as Mass was beginning.

She must have left the cafeteria not long after I graduated from the eighth grade. By the time I graduated from college and was working at our family business in Boonetown, she was in her early or mid-sixties. I was lucky that she had opened her own little lunch spot.

Alfie's Lunch Box was a small place, in an old building on the square, with maybe fifteen tables and lots of regulars. Alfie made the best desserts ever, and served really good homemade meals. Every day she had a special, and my favorite was the chicken casserole on Thursdays. Most amazingly, she did all the cooking with just a couple of electric skillets and an old residential range. She made all the pies and cakes for the restaurant at home in the evenings. She seemed to work continually. She not only served lunches from her little restaurant, she also did catering.

Our church was planning a huge celebration dinner for the 100th anniversary of the church building. Alfie was asked to provide the meal. I was delighted to hear this because I knew it would be good. But apparently one woman in the parish wasn't as happy.

Elaine was a rather loud, overbearing woman who liked to share her feelings freely. Elaine had made it clear to several people that she wanted another caterer because she didn't get enough to eat at Alfie's. (I had always gotten plenty to eat there.) But this lady was the same woman that paid her lawn guy with cucumbers from her garden. So, you might say she was miserly: if she paid for a meal, she wanted more than her money's worth.

On the night of the big dinner, my family and I were seated at a table right beside the table where Elaine and her family were seated. That night they were serving sliced roast beef with gravy, rice, green beans and another vegetable as I recall. There were several hundred in attendance, so in order to serve everyone quickly, they asked the group at each table to stand and proceed to the buffet line in order, according to how the tables were arranged. Because of the proximity of our tables, I was just a few folks behind Elaine in line.

Now, I had already heard the rumor about Elaine's complaint. I had also heard that Alfie was aware of it, too.

The catering staff was dressing the plates for each person, handing them out as everyone proceeded through the buffet line. Just as they were getting to Elaine, I saw the kitchen door fly open.

Alfie's daughter came rushing over with a special plate of food, put it right in front of Elaine and said, "This is compliments of Alfie."

The plate was stacked so high with roast beef and vegetables it looked like a serving platter. There had to have been a couple of pounds of beef there. Elaine seemed unfazed. I don't think she got the joke. As a matter of fact, she seemed kind of proud of her over-flowing plate.

We had been given forty-five or so minutes to eat and then had been subjected to a very long and pretty boring program about the history of the parish. About ten p.m. as things were wrapping up, I happened to think about Elaine. I turned around to see her still working her knife and fork through that roast beef like a hungry lumberjack. She was chewing just as fast as she could. She had made it through most of the two-inch high stack of beef and seemed to be intent on finishing. I elbowed my brother and my mother, and we all got the giggles. We could not stop. We speculated that her jaws would be incredible sore the next day.

I really don't think Elaine ever got the joke. I think she just thought it was her lucky night. But we sure got it. By far the best part of the evening. From that point on I knew that Alfie and her daughter were not ones to be messed with. Somehow that made eating at Alfie's more exciting.

Back to that day at Alfie's. Maggie and I were trying to solve the mystery of Mr. Feldman's companion. While Maggie and I were pondering, I remembered hearing Mrs. Feldman mention a twin sister who lived out of town. Ah! We figured that must be who the mystery woman was. The woman sort of resembled his wife and could have easily been a sister.

But then another week passed and she was still eating with him. No sign of his wife either. And then the Feldmans' son started showing up for lunch with them. He didn't seem to notice that his Mom had been replaced. Maggie and I were really beginning to wonder if Mr. Feldman dropped his wife and found a new companion a period of a few weeks.

Finally, we asked the waitress if she knew what happened to Mrs. Feldman.

The waitress didn't understand what we meant. "She is eating there with Mr. Feldman and her son right now," she said.

We protested. "But we've seen Mrs. Feldman here a lot. That's not her."

"She just had a face lift, I think," the waitress said.

You think? Was she kidding?

She was totally unrecognizable to either of us, and we saw the woman every day.

Mrs. Feldman was known to be obsessed with her appearance and her clothes and jewelry. She never, ever wore the same thing twice, (said it gave her hives), so we would have never been able to figure it out from familiar outfits.

Mrs. Feldman and her husband had purchased a successful jewelry business in town and seemed to be quite well off. The reason I knew that Mrs. Feldman had a twin sister was because the sister was rumored to be a kleptomaniac. It was widely talked about around town. My hairstylist told me that Mr. Feldman came in her shop shortly after they moved to town and informed her that his wife, Mrs. Feldman, had a twin sister and she was a bit of a kleptomaniac. He said that she visited town often and they would recognize her because she looked a lot like his wife, and would be stealing things. He said to just total-up anything his sister-in-law took, and call him after she left with the merchandise. He would come by and write them a check. Other merchants told me the same thing, so apparently, he had been all over town. He was a devoted brother-in-law, no doubt. Not sure why the merchants put up with this because she might have been stealing stuff they never noticed, but surprisingly they all went along. I think she was likely a very good customer when she wasn't stealing, so the gains probably outweighed the losses.

But after Maggie and I got the facelift intel on Mrs. Feldman, we still had a problem: Staring.

We could not stop staring.

We kept trying to figure out what parts of her old

face were still in there and where they had been moved to.

Maggie and I were also speculating if the facelift, being so drastic, was done to set her apart, so to speak, from the twin sister. (I had heard "the twin" had been banned from several stores in Nashville.) Now Mrs. Feldman could go in and not be confused with her twin sister. If that was her goal, it may have worked, but I think it triggered a long-term obsession with plastic surgery.

From that point on, we noticed her come in bruised and limping and squinting on a regular basis. She began to talk freely about all the work she had had done. She was the first person I heard of getting butt implants and calf implants. She said she could hardly walk after those. She said she had a tummy tuck, breast implants and more work done on her face and eyes. If she was unrecognizable after the face lift, now she was ready for the witness protection program. I think all the changes to her appearance were probably more about her desire to look good than to hide her identity, but either way, it seemed to make her feel really good about herself, so I guess it was worth the pain.

Later that same year, (I'm not sure if it was the summer of Mrs. Feldman's new face or the fall of her new butt) another woman swept into Alfie's like a long-lost relative that had been trapped for decades on the set of the Andy Griffith show. This woman wasn't as fashion-forward as Mrs. Feldman. No, this woman was more Aunt Bea than Mary Tyler Moore. But she knew how to work a room.

She wore lots of floral, full-skirted dresses, and pinned her hair in a bun. She always seemed to float around the room, and her dresses seemed to have built-in fans. On the first day she arrived, she stopped by my table and managed to tell me more about herself than I really needed to know. In our brief conversation, I learned that she was very involved in her conservative Church-of-Christ church, and planned to be involved in her new Boonetown church as well. She was moving to town. She had met an old boyfriend from Boonetown at her fiftieth-class reunion and had moved to Boonetown to marry him. He was divorced and available at the time, and she didn't waste a second. At least that's what I gathered. By the end of day three, she was on a first name basis with every regular.

Her prospective groom was not. He was a local accountant and hardly ever spoke to anyone, even as they continued to come in the restaurant. They were an odd couple, but he seemed to be on cloud nine, so whatever she was doing for him was working like a tonic.

She revealed in another conversation that she had a few prior marriages and divorces. I was a bit skeptical because I think most southern churches, especially conservative ones, really frown on divorce. But she assured everyone that all three of her divorces were biblical, so they were AOK with the church. I had never heard of a biblical divorce, but apparently it is a real thing. Her most recent husband was deceased, so the two class-reunion-sweethearts were free to marry and they did within a month or two.

This was pure conjecture on my part, but it seemed to me that she had this process of finding a man, moving to his town and marrying him down to a science.

My friend Maggie heard that they had immediately bought a double-wide tombstone and had it placed on a two-person plot at the Memory Gardens, even before the wedding. I would call this putting the cart before the horse, but I guess since she had such bad luck with husbands, maybe she wanted to be sure she had someone to spend eternity with.

Of course, Maggie and I went by to check it out.

It had two big intertwined hearts carved on the front, and it said something like, "At Long Last, Together for Forever". Then it had both their names and birth dates engraved at the bottom, just waiting for their eminent demise. I know this might have seemed incredibly romantic to some folks, but as for me, I viewed it as a bad omen for the new husband. I just could not help but wonder how many of those double-wide tombstones were left in cemeteries across the state with her name on one side and a man buried beneath the other side. But according to her, they were deeply in love, and fate had brought them together again, so what do I know? I was happy they had found each other, but kept an eye on the tombstone just the same.

Have you ever noticed when someone from a larger city moves to a small town, they always think the locals have just been waiting there, desperate for someone fabulous to come in and share their taste and ideas with all the poor, downtrodden townsfolk? Well, another new woman named KellyAnn arrived in Boonetown that year and promptly let us all know that she was indeed fabulous. At least she thought so.

She appeared at Alfie's and made it clear to all of us that she was the new trendsetter in town and we should all take note. She had purchased a large older home in town (one of the few really nice old homes left standing) and was planning to convert it into Boonetown's first bed-and-breakfast.

On her first sweep through Alfie's Lunch Box, she made sure to let all us regulars know that she was often confused with Tammy Wynette, but not to worry, it was just little-ol', down-to-earth KellyAnn. Personally, I was having no problem telling them apart: they were both blonde and female, but for me the similarities ended there.

I also noticed that every day she wore one color from head to toe. One day it would be pink, one day maybe lavender, but always one color: blouse, skirt, jacket, dyed shoes, scarf, and hair bow. I think she needed the hair bows to cover the spots where she attached her hair pieces, but I cannot say that with certainty. I know they were hair pieces because her hair got longer and shorter from day to day. She definitely was caught in some country-music-fashion time warp. (My mom's neighbor, Pearl, used to refer to this as the "costume effect", wearing one color head to toe. But Pearl was never able to achieve it like KellyAnn. You have to fully commit, with the hair ornament and the dyed shoes, to really make it work.)

When KellyAnn found out I was a designer, she made it a point, every day at lunch, to talk so I could overhear her plans for the B & B. I would get an earful. And, according to her, it was going to be something: expert renovation, fine period furnishings, the best linens, and of course, the best hostess. We all wondered where the money for all this was coming from. There was some mention of a husband, but he was never seen. He was still living "elsewhere." KellyAnn didn't work, and to my knowledge had not had a country music career, and she never mentioned any other career or sources of income, so we figured she must have married well.

The renovations took close to a year. When they were finally done, KellyAnn was walking on air at the Lunch Box. Some of the people that had seen the renovations had given glowing reports. Others, not so glowing. KellyAnn said she had restored the old mansion to its former glory.

I was secretly dying to see it. And as luck would have it, my friend Maggie was KellyAnn's banker and she had been invited to stop by and bring friends. So, one night Maggie and I and a few other friends went by for a tour.

Even though she knew we were coming, it took forever to get her to the door. When she finally arrived at the door, she was a touch drunk. That went pretty much unnoticed because Maggie and I were the only ones in our group that weren't a little intoxicated as well. Apparently, everyone (except Maggie and I) had been out for dinner and cocktails. They were all asking lots of questions and listening intently to her stories. Meanwhile, Maggie and I were free to walk around and check things out. The thought, "high class brothel" did pop into my head, but I tried to keep an open mind.

KellyAnn had obviously spent a lot on the renovations, but her choices left me puzzled. She covered up all the old hardwood flooring with wall-to-wall carpeting, and that's an unforgivable sin in my book. All the wallpaper was very shiny with sparkles in it, and sparkly wallpaper is also pretty high on my list of no-no's, so I wasn't really finding much to like. Everything had this plastic look about it.

At Alfie's, she had often mentioned all the period antiques she placed in the house. But Maggie and I were having a hard time finding them. Turns out, a lot of the furniture she was pointing to and calling "antique" was actually about a year old. We knew this because we had seen it all at Dings and Bings, down near the state line. Dings and Bings was an outlet store that sold returned and damaged catalog merchandise. Apparently KellyAnn had done a lot of shopping there.

The master suite was all done in deep green and hot pink. The bedroom had more of the shiny, sparkling wallpaper and a bed with a large, gold-plastic, swirly headboard.

In the master bath, KellyAnn proudly pointed out the two nude portraits of herself hanging over the hot-pink clawfoot tub. Surveying the room, there was also a hot pink toilet, hot pink bidet, and hot pink vanity, as well as crystal wall sconces bouncing light about the room. The 'high class brothel' thought crossed my mind a second time.

When KellyAnn started telling (slurring a bit) about posing for her nude portraits, one front and one rear view, Maggie and I lost it. We got tickled. I mean really tickled. So tickled, we had to go in another room and shut the door. I'm not sure how much KellyAnn could hear, but she had to have heard some of our laughter.

It's really embarrassing when you arrive somewhere with a group of liquored-up folks and then end up acting worse than any of them. We were the ones who acted worse. None of our friends gave a hoot about the house, they just came along because they had nothing else to do on a Saturday night. And they had not heard KellyAnn go on and on at Alfie's about the fine B & B she was opening, the fine antiques and how impressed Boonetown would be. So this wasn't funny to them.

But Maggie and I had heard all those things, and we just couldn't take it. There KellyAnn was, wearing a head-to-toe, leopard-print lounging ensemble (thus achieving a nice "costume effect") and I could not keep my composure. The drinkers in our group were quite embarrassed by our behavior that night, and they had a point, but they had also embarrassed us often enough, so I figured it was our turn.

I guess the pressure of being the most fabulous person in town became too much or maybe business was slow. It wasn't long until KellyAnn sold the place and moved away. She included all the fine antiques in the sale.

The woman with all the biblical divorces buried her (new) old flame underneath one side of the double-wide tombstone in the cemetery just a couple of years later, and she moved on to another class reunion and another husband. So he was left lying there alone, now and forever, I suspect. I also suspect another tombstone went up somewhere in another city or state, with another husband's name carved in between etched hearts.

Mr. Feldman died unexpectedly a few years after all of his wife's plastic surgery. I wonder who went around writing checks for the twin's stolen goods. Come to think of it, I never actually saw Mrs. Feldman and her twin sister together…hmmm.

I guess we'll never know. She left Boonetown, and to my knowledge, was never heard from again.

After the big church dinner, Elaine suddenly became a regular at Alfie's. It was short lived though. I was watching, and I could see the let-down expression on her face every time she received a normal portion of roast beef. I think by the second week, she finally put it together that she had fallen victim to a practical joke. She never returned to Alfie's.

Alfie retired about fifteen years ago. I was a regular till the very end.

I miss the Lunch Box. I miss Alfie, too. Such good food. The floorshow wasn't bad either.

MOM

If there was one way to describe my mom, it was "on duty". Always, on duty. Her responsibilities never ended. She never had a break. Whether it was putting three meals a day on the table for the family, or doing all our laundry, or keeping the house clean without any outside help, she did all of that and more. She would spend hours at the sewing machine making almost all of the clothes for herself and my sister, and then transport us to all those lessons and practices we needed to attend. She would can and freeze food from the garden all summer so that we could enjoy it all winter.

I could see the weary look in her eyes as my dad planted a larger garden every year. He loved growing lots of food and he loved growing his prize tomatoes, but it was Mom who had to harvest most of it. And then prep it. And then use the heavy pressure cooker to seal those quarts of green beans that we all loved so much. Every year Dad would promise to put out a smaller garden, especially after all of us children had left home. But he never did. And Mom, being a depression baby, would never let anything go to waste.

Her parents lived in the country and were still poor farmers, just getting by. Unlike the grandparents of today, my grandparents were of no help to Mom with her family. Actually, just the opposite. Mom would drive to their home in the country, every week or so, to help them with the house work or canning or whatever was needed. Mom would have them at our house for every holiday meal and special occasion.

But my mom wasn't just available to her parents and Dad and us children. She was a caretaker for so many others as well. She was the neighborhood "angel of mercy", it would seem, since she was constantly getting called to help out several little old ladies that lived nearby.

We lived near the Catholic church. Mom and Dad had built a new home there. Most of the other homes in the area were older, and so were the residents. The area around the church was an old German settlement, and both of my parents were of German ancestry. Mom genuinely cared for people, especially people who seemed to have been forgotten by society. Widows and "old maids," (as they were called back then) always seemed to call on Mom when they needed help with groceries, or a ride to the doctor, or some help at home. And she always responded.

As a child I would be irritated when we had to stop at the grocery store and pick something up for one of the ladies. I didn't understand that Mom was probably the only person they could count on.

Mrs. Andre was one of the little old ladies that counted on Mom whenever she was in distress, and that was pretty often. She would call Mom in the afternoon to chat, and Mom could not get her off the phone. Mrs. Andre would talk on and on about Daddy (her deceased husband), or her son, John-the-

Third. She always called him John-the-Third, never just John. Around our house, we referred to John-the-Third as John-the-Turd, since he never seemed to call his mom, or to come from California to visit her.

One day, Dad brought home a copy of *The Tennessean* newspaper and couldn't wait to show it to my mom. There was an article about a California man who was driving across the state, pulling a trailer with a huge boat behind on it. This wasn't just a little fishing boat. This was one of those large boats, with sleeping quarters underneath the top deck. The paper included a photograph of this once-beautiful vessel, news-worthy now because it had flown off the trailer and landed on the roof of the car.

Apparently, the driver had to make a sudden stop and the boat came forward, airborne I suppose, and completely flattened the car. It's a miracle the driver survived the accident. The article went on to say that the man driving the car was a highly decorated pilot and war veteran who had made many successful bombing flights during his time in World War II. The accident had occurred somewhere in California, but the wire picked up the photo. It had been printed in every newspaper across the country.

The driver of the car was John-the-Turd.

We never knew if Mrs. Andre saw the article. I don't think Mom showed it to her. Mom figured that the event might give John-the-Turd a reason to call. But we never got wind of that. If he *had* called Mrs. Andre, we were sure she would have called Mom to give her all the details.

Back then telephones were not portable and certainly not wireless, so if Mom had gotten that call, or any others, she would be stuck at the desk in the living room. We didn't have a kitchen wall phone. I remember many times Mom would be trying to get

Mrs. Andre off the phone, but as usual she would not stop talking about Daddy and John-the-Third. Mom would hold up the little sign she had made that said, "Go ring the doorbell". I or my sister would go to the front door and ring the doorbell. Mom would then say, "Mrs. Andre I've got to go. There is someone at the door." Mrs. Andre must've thought we were the most popular family in the neighborhood because every time she called, we had drop-in's.

The afternoon calls from Mrs. Andre were annoying, but Mother could deal with that. What she couldn't deal with were the night time calls.

The phone would ring in the middle of the night and Mrs. Andre would be screaming, "Jesus, Jesus, help me, help me I'm dying, Louise I'm dying, I'm dying, you've got to take me to the hospital, I'm dying."

So, Mom would get out of bed, get dressed, and head over to her house, help Mrs. Andre get dressed and into the car and take her to the emergency room, with Mrs. Andre hysterically screaming for Jesus to take her home the entire time. I guess in the beginning Mom would have been quite distressed by this, but after about the fifteenth time, Mom knew she was just lonely and scared.

Mom always said the minute Mrs. Andre got to the local hospital she would begin to calm down, because she knew she would have some company for a few days. Once they checked her into the room — back then they kept you at least a few days no matter what was wrong — Mrs. Andre would ask my mother to come close to her ear and would whisper, "Louise, take out my diamond ear-screws and hide them in your purse so the nurses won't steal them." Mom said that she would know for sure that Mrs. Andre really was dying if she did *not* ask her to remove those diamond ear-screws.

One night, Mrs. Andre called begging for Mother to come take her to the hospital, and it happened that my new car was parked behind Mom's Caprice Classic. My car was a compact red Chevrolet Chevette. It was very small, much too small for a six-foot-six boy, but I was still proud of it. Rather than get me up to move it, Mother decided to take my car to pick up Mrs. Andre.

My mother wasn't feeling well that night and she asked my sister, who was in nursing school, to go along and help her. I think Mom thought it would be good experience for her. I'm not sure my sister felt the same.

When Mom got Mrs. Andre loaded into the car, Mrs. Andre observed her new surroundings and (in between screaming "Jesus, take me home to Daddy!" and "Help me Lord, I'm dying!") looked over at my mother and said, "Louise, this is the cutest little car I've ever seen."

With that comment, Mother knew immediately there was nothing wrong. She didn't even have to wait for her to ask for her to remove her diamond ear-screws.

My mom, and also my dad for that matter, were very capable people. Pretty much anything that came up during the day could be handled by one or the other of them. When the church decided to add fried chicken to the meal at their big annual fundraiser, it was cooked on our carport. Dad rigged up gas burners under two big black kettles and Mom organized a crew to clean and batter the chicken. She used her famous double batter technique on the chicken before it was fried. It was a huge hit, and was served every year from then on and it is still being served today. After a few years of cooking it on our carport, the cooking setup was moved to the school property, but our carport is where it all started. Chicken for seven or eight hundred people? No problem.

For the most part, Mom was very calm. But there was one thing that would cause Mom a great deal of distress and a shocking amount of rage.

Snakes.

She had been bitten by a rattlesnake when she was a little girl on the farm and almost died before they could get her to the doctor in town. Even forty years later, one of her ankles was still a bit larger than the other and she attributed that to the snake bite. So when she would see a snake, she would be both terrified and enraged.

One time, a snake had somehow gotten into the house and into her bedroom. She thought my dad had left a belt on the floor and almost picked it up before realizing it was a black snake. Knowing she would never be able to sleep in the house again if that snake got away (and not one to call for a man to come take care of her), she first pulverized it with a broom until it was lifeless, then took her garden hoe and carried it to the driveway, at which point she chopped it into so many tiny pieces one would have never known it was a snake. When I got home from school, she said I should go look at the snake she found inside the house, but I was hard-pressed to find one. I was mistakenly looking for a snake, not a couple hundred, scattered, pea-size pieces of snake confetti.

When my family moved into a big new house, Mom and her next-door neighbor became good friends. Pearl was a sweet lady and a good cook, but she would watch my mom with utter amazement. Pearl and her husband thought Mom and Dad were magicians or something because they could fix things and take care of just about anything around the house. Pearl always sent her things out for alterations, or repairs, or hired someone to make her draperies. She couldn't believe that Mom could do all that herself. Dad was also handy. He could fix the heat, or repair the lawnmower, or put a new alternator in his truck. It's not that Mom and Dad could do things no one else could do, it's just that they could do so many different things and do them all well.

Perhaps Mom's best hidden talent was that she was a shrewd judge of character. She could spot a fake or a liar at fifty paces. We used to tease her about being too quick to put a label on someone she just saw or met, but over the years she was proven right over and over.

The one thing my mother did *not* do well was kiss anyone's butt.

At the Catholic school, a lot of the mothers spent a lot of time doing just that. Some would spend lots of time buttering up the nuns in order to get preferential treatment for their kids. Since Mom was not up for that sort of thing, I was usually not one of the chosen few to star in school plays, or be singled out (in a good way) at school.

But one year, I think I was talking to my friends a little too loud about how I had "never been on the Christmas float because we never had the nuns over to our house for dinner."

The next week, I was chosen to be one of the Wisemen on the Christmas float. (I learned then that my voice carried, a quality that has haunted me all my life.) Mom went right into action, making me this long, green, satin king's robe, and a really cool silver crown. I think I had the best costume, but I sure didn't get any compliments from the nuns.

The year I decided to become a ventriloquist, I asked for a Charlie McCarthy dummy. I was extremely disappointed when he arrived with only one, really ugly, orange suit. Again, Mom went into action and helped me make him several suits to wear when he performed by my side in the living room.

Mom even made me a leisure suit when I couldn't find one to fit. (Don't judge: It was the seventies.)

While Mom was always available for her family, there was one episode that shook things up a bit.

Our family attended Holy Rosary Catholic Church and we went to the Catholic school. It was a conservative parish, even by Catholic standards. But this was the seventies, and there was a sexual revolution going on. Or so I was told. You would have never known it from our parish. I don't think we even had one divorce among all our members.

However, there was this one couple that attended church there regularly. They were younger than my parents, by a few years anyway, and seemed to be a bit more free-spirited about things. Let's call them Chuck and Rhonda.

Chuck and Rhonda invited this other couple, we'll call them John and Linda, to start attending our church. So John and Linda began attending weekly. This was very unusual, because people don't just "start attending" a Catholic church. New members typically either marry into the church, or are born into a Catholic family. So, this "started attending" business attracted some attention.

The two couples would generally sit in the same pew and, after a while, no one thought much of it. There was a rumor going around that John had been divorced a couple of times, which meant he would probably not be able to join the church officially, but he was till free to attend.

One Sunday, things were different. Chuck was sitting by Linda, and John was sitting by Rhonda.

Now, it isn't like they were just all sitting in a row and somehow got shifted around. No. They were sitting as two separate couples, but with reversed spouses.

This did create some chatter among the other attendees. But things didn't really take a turn until the next week...when they did that same thing again.

By that second Sunday, word had begun circulating around town that they had literally swapped wives. But people were still skeptical.

Then, by the third Sunday, it was a full-blown scandal.

Now, this wasn't a situation like at the Presbyterian Church around the corner, where two couples in the church got divorced, and then two of those ex-spouses married each other, and then a couple of years later the remaining two exes got married.

No. This was a full-on, weekend wife swap.

One week it was Chuck and Rhonda, and then just like that, the next it was Chuck and Linda. No muss. No fuss. No divorces. Done deal. And, they had the unmitigated gall to keep coming to church as if nothing had happened.

My mother was shocked, as was the rest of the parish. Let's just say for the next few weeks Mom was *off* duty. She was now on full-time phone duty: This needed to be discussed by the ladies of the parish. Our church and our little town hadn't had anything this juicy to discuss *ever*! And it was happening right there, three pews up on the left at the Catholic Church. Right under the nose of the statue of Mary. Holy Mother of God, indeed!

Since back then there was no social media, or Facebook, or texting, or e-mail, all gossip had to be transferred via the telephone. Mom was pretty much stuck at the desk in the living room for hours. This was one of the few times she let anyone else in her kitchen to do any cooking. She would throw out some cooking directions to my sister or I mid-phone call, then get right back to the wife swap gossip.

It took a week or two for Mom to return to her duties. After a month or so, the phone calls finally did begin to slow up. I guess everyone just got used to the two new couples sitting together in church. People kept thinking it wouldn't last, waiting to see if either of them returned to their old seat with their old spouse, but they never did. Both couples remained together until one or the other of the spouses died. So all in all, one could say the wife swap was successful. Holy Rosary moved on.

As our family business became more successful, Dad became a member of the Boonetown Country Club. He loved golf and he loved hanging out in the clubhouse. Before long he was the President of the Country Club.

Mom hated going to those functions with my dad at the country club. She never thought she fit in with that group of people. She grew up in the country on a farm, about as poor as you could get. She never had any new clothes and was lucky to get a new pair of shoes at the beginning of the school year. She walked to school because the public-school buses would not transport Catholic kids to school at that time. She went to the private Catholic school because they were members of the Catholic church, not because they were well-off. Her parents usually didn't have the money to pay the meager tuition they charged.

I remember Mom saying that most days she had to

carry her lunch, since she didn't have any money to buy lunch, and some days all her mother would have to put in her lunch pail would be a hard biscuit. She would often say, "I don't know what people mean when they talk about the good old days, as far as I am concerned, there was nothing good about them."

But Mom didn't dwell on it. She'd make a comment like that and then change the conversation.

I think most people never get over what happens to them in their childhood. I know growing up in that kind of poverty stuck with my mother all her life. No matter how well the business was doing, Mom conserved and saved, and seldom spent money on herself. It didn't matter that they were getting ahead. In her mind, that could change at any moment and they could be right back where they were in the beginning: two broke farm kids trying to raise a family and make a house payment. She never ever forgot that feeling. I think she always felt like that poor girl that didn't have lunch money. So, if she saw someone in need, or struggling, especially an elderly lady or a young mother, she reached out and helped in some way.

Mom had a wicked dry wit, and she was also a strong life-long Democrat. Very near the end of her life, she was very sick and dehydrated from years of chemotherapy. My mother never complained, and she handled cancer with a great deal of dignity. She never wanted to be a burden, and hated for any of us to have to take time out of our schedules to take her to the doctor or hospital, but I always knew she was really glad we were there.

One time, she had to go in the hospital for a couple of days and fluids were ordered. I spent the night in the room with her after they had been giving her fluids all day but the doctor had not ordered a catheter. Needless to say, we were both up all night, but she was a real trouper as usual. I know she was terribly weak and exhausted, but she tried not to show it. George Bush was the president at the time and, every once in a while, something would pop up on the TV about him.

She looked up from the bed and squinted at the TV. "Is that George Bush? Is he in Texas on the ranch again?"

"Yes," I said, "it's him."

Without missing a beat, she said, "I wish he would step in a great big pile of horse shit."

I think she knew I needed a laugh.

We both got tickled, and I thought to remind her of another time that she had been in the hospital many years ago.

She had been scheduled to have hemorrhoid surgery and had been dreading it very much. She made it through the surgery just fine. Later that day, Mom was still groggy and very uncomfortable, in the recovery room. She was on a lot of pain medicine and awoke to hear nurses screaming, sobbing and crying in the hall outside. She didn't know what to think. Had she died? Was she looking down from somewhere above hearing her family mourn her death? Or was she about to die and no one wanted to tell her?

She continued to hear sobbing in the halls and couldn't find a nurse anywhere in the recovery room to ask. She was becoming upset. Finally, my sister came in to check on her and told her the news.

Elvis had died. The news had just come on television. The nurses were distraught. Mom was a bit distraught, too, because she never really liked Elvis, and she got absolutely no service from any of the staff for the rest of the stay. All the nurses did was stand at the nurse's station and cry.

My mother had never been one to use a four-letter word. She was always a lady, but the hemorrhoid surgery changed that. Not a lot, but she did let a few new words enter her vocabulary. We were a bit shocked by this at home and made a comment or two about it. She said that while she was in the hospital, an untold number of people had examined her rear end, before, during and after surgery. She said, "I guess, when you show your ass, you lose your class."

It became a big family joke that Mom lost her class when she had that surgery, but nothing could have been further from the truth.

"Class" is something you either have or you don't.

It's so funny to me now, watching all these "housewives" and "influencers" with TV shows, trying to portray themselves as classy, taking a camera crew with them every time they think might do a good deed. But as far as I'm concerned, class, and integrity for that matter, are formed by the things you do when no one is watching. And how you treat people, especially those who can do nothing for you in return.

Mom treated everyone with respect, except maybe people who had an inflated sense of self-importance. The things my mom did for others throughout her life went largely unnoticed, except of course, by her family and by the people she was helping.

She never felt the need to tell everyone, she just showed up and did the work.

Making Do

As I traveled weekly from Boonetown to Nashville for weekends at my condo, I began to notice more and more campers parked over in a field just outside of Boonetown. At first it was two or three, then it was four or five, and the number continued to grow. This was really right in the middle of Amish country. I thought someone might be buying and selling them, or just letting folks park them there. There certainly wasn't any other reason they might be there.

But then a sign showed up along the highway and it sort of answered my question.

"Restful Acres Campground"

I was confused.

First of all, I thought Restful Acres might be an appropriate name for a cemetery, but not really a campground. The area in question was just an empty lot, maybe a couple acres total, and no trees to be found. I decided to circle back and check it out up close.

It didn't look any different up close than from the highway.

Basically, it was a horseshoe-shaped drive, with parking spaces along it. A building at the back housed an office and some rest rooms. The campers were parked very close together, looked like eight or ten feet apart. I did notice that some trees had been planted, but none of them had reached the height of the campers yet. So Restful Acres was really more of a restful parking lot in plain view of the highway.

I couldn't imagine that it would succeed (especially considering there was a beautiful park nearby with lovely wooded campgrounds). But every time I drove by, I noticed more campers.

Then they added cabins. Around back. They must have bought some of those little wooden storage buildings from Home Depot. You know, the ones that have that little front porch. They had two very small rooms, but no bathrooms.

I know this because, by now, I had been asking my friends about the Restful Acres Campground fairly regularly. We would speculate as to whether or not anyone was renting the cabins, or the covered wagons. Oh, did I mention that they had covered wagons you could also rent to sleep in? Around back, by the cabins.

So, for my fiftieth birthday my friends rented me a cabin...for the whole night. You do have to bring your own sheets, but the bath house was quite nice and really clean. They hosted a little party there for me on my little front porch. Guests were limited due to space, but it was fun. The covered wagons didn't have mattresses like the cabins, so I was glad they spent the extra money to get a cabin. (And climbing out of the wagon in the middle of the night to use the bathroom might have been a bit jarring.)

Apparently Restful Acres was just what the doctor ordered, because it stays full all the time. I think they are often in an overflow situation with RVs these days. I can't speak for the cabins or the wagons, but the place looks very busy. Some of the trees have actually grown taller than the RVs now, so it has taken on a bit more of a "campground" look, but it is still right beside a busy highway, something that no one seems to notice but me. The owner told us that it had always been his dream to own a campground and, even though the location seemed odd to me, he made it work. That is what I admire about people in Boonetown.

They make do.

Nana lived not far from Restful Acres. Not my nana. She was sort of everyone's nana. Nana was actually a guest on Johnny Carson, David Letterman, and several other popular late-night talk shows back in the eighties. (For those of you too young to remember: Johnny was before Leno, and Leno before Fallon.) Back in those days, being on Johnny Carson was a very big deal. This was before there were seven hundred channels to choose from, and there were no blogs or podcasts or web series. Johnny was it as far as late night went.

The woman we called Nana lived just north of Boonetown, right between the Amish country and Restful Acres. Well, Restful Acres wasn't there yet, but she lived near the location. She became famous because she had started her own television network from her garage.

She had one of those big satellite dishes that were popular when people first started to try to find an alternative to cable. She said she kept the rest of her equipment in the garage, including the receiver. I'm not sure how she was able to re-air the programming from other larger networks, but she did. She would broadcast Atlanta Braves baseball games that were being aired on Ted Turner's network. This was before many homes had access to those types of cable channels, so she was popular with many sports buffs.

She also attended all the local high school sporting events and recorded them with her camcorder. This was back when camcorders, or video recorders, still had the cassette tapes you recorded on. (For those of you too young to get these terms, look it up online under ancient history.)

Her sports coverage was non-edited. You could hear conversations of the people sitting around the camera, and then you could see her hand reach over the lens to turn off the camera at the end of the game. There was no editing room, or any splicing together, or cutting-out of the rough parts. This was just recorded and then played on-air. I'd call it no-frills programming. No one complained about the lack of editing because most of the viewers had never seen their children or themselves on TV before and it was a fun new source of entertainment.

I was amazed that she was able to keep programming going on the TV while she was out covering all the ball games, dance recitals and parades in town. I could imagine her calling her next door neighbor when she knew the tape of the recent Bobcat basketball game was about to finish, and asking them to run over to her house, let the dog out to potty, and pop in another tape to fill the gap until she made it home.

She was sixty-ish at the time, always in a rush, and a bit disheveled. Her glasses were always dangling on a chain around her neck and she spent a lot of time putting them on and taking them off. Her hair was usually thrown up in a last-minute bun. But really, who has time for the hair salon when you are a busy television executive?

I didn't know Nana, but I knew she had some children and grandchildren that were occasionally involved with her in the television station. She also had a bowling team. The reason I knew this was because our family construction business also had a bowling team, in the same league. My brother and a few of his buddies bowled once a week for our company's team, but I was not a team member.

One particular night our team was bowling against Nana's network. I just happened to drop by that night to take in the game. It turned out that, because of the way the teams laid out with handicaps and such, my brother was bowling against Nana. He was probably early thirties and she was probably mid-sixties.

My brother was extremely competitive. He was tall and very strong. What he lacked in finesse in bowling, he certainly made up for in power and strength.

Each time my brother went up to bowl, he would throw the ball so hard, it literally would not touch the alley until about three feet in front of the pins. The pins would explode into the air and hit the back wall of the alley. Yet, against all possible odds, one pin would still be standing over at the side, wobbling just a little, but never falling. This happened so many times that evening it was hard to believe. Every time, he would throw the ball harder and the pins would make a larger explosion, but one or two stubborn pins would remain standing as if they were glued to the floor.

Nana's taunting didn't help things at all. She'd let out a "whoop!", when he failed to get a strike. His face would turn an even deeper shade of red and he'd clench his fists.

Nana had a different approach. She would pick up the ball, drag it over to her lane, sort of holding it between her legs, and then just drop it. Then, we would all watch it with utter amazement as it wobbled all the way down the alley. We were convinced it would not even make it to the first pin or end up in the gutter. But no, we were proven wrong again and again.

With barely enough force to move the first pin, tapping it only hard enough to make it wobble, it would teeter back and forth eventually falling, knocking down another couple of pins on the way. Then a domino effect would begin taking down pin after pin, until all ten were resting on the hardwood.

Nana would jump up and down and whoop and holler as she high-fived her team. My brother would turn several more shades of red and press his fist so hard into the plastic seats that he left his imprint. We were debating amongst the team whether he would have a heart attack or a stroke first. The madder my brother got, the harder he threw the bowling ball. I swear a few times I don't think it ever touched down on the floor before it hit the pins.

He might have made a strike that night, but I can't remember it. It was like those corner pins were nailed down. Nana on the other hand set a new personal-best.

Nana produced and hosted her own talk show. You didn't have to worry about being a great conversationalist with Nana. She loved to laugh and tell stories and did most all of the talking no matter what the subject. Her sidekick would fill in the occasional blank, and her guest might get to plug an upcoming event, but Nana did the rest. When it was time for the episode to end, you would see Nana's hand move across the screen to find the off switch on the camera, and your TV screen at home would go black until she popped in another video cassette.

Occasionally, the station would just go off the air for a couple of weeks and we didn't know why until

160

she returned to the air and told us she had accidentally backed over the receiver with her car or, a tornado had hit her satellite dish, or some other such disaster. Nana never sugar coated anything. I think that's why she became popular.

She also took her talk show to remote locations. One Saturday, I was home from college watching TV with my mom. We decided to pop in on Nana and see what she was doing. She was airing a remote broadcast from the local nursing home. It was a Christmas Special. Nana and the nursing home had brought in some entertainment for the residents. The residents had mostly been wheeled into the activity room to partake of the entertainment. One entertainer was a high-pitched, gospel music singer, accompanied by herself on piano and her seven-year-old grandson on toy guitar. I don't think he had had any lessons on the guitar at this point, but he played boldly, confidently, and loudly. I think he had gotten the confidence from Grandma who also sang and played very loudly, and very confidently, without a lot of concern for things like pitch or staying in time. I never identified a point at which both of them were playing in the same key—or the same song for that matter—but they managed to plow through several selections.

Over in the lower corner of the screen, I saw a couple of the residents trying to wheel themselves out the side door, but the nurses turned them around and wheeled them back. My mother and I were horrified and wanted to go stage a break-out in the activity room, but we knew this had to have been previously recorded. There was a reading of some poetry and some more carols with piano accompaniment before the broadcast ended and you finally saw Nana's arm move across the screen to the off button. The sight of her arm was way overdue.

I must give credit where credit is due, because I have no idea, given the limited technology available at that time, how she was able to pull it off. I'm not sure whether it came through our cable or just through the air, but we got Nana's network at my home, and most of the homes in the county did as well. I guess you could say it was a community service because I can't remember any advertisers, and I can't figure out how she could have made any money.

Boonetown was always trying to boost tourism. Somebody brought up a new idea. They decided to start putting the hand and foot prints of all the famous Boonevillians in the sidewalk, out in front of the Daniel Boone Theater, (our old local movie theater). I supposed they were thinking this would be a local Walk of Stars like the original one in Hollywood. In theory, I suppose this could work and become a tourist attraction...of sorts.

The city did manage to convince a local man who had become a fairly famous actor (he had appeared in some well-known movies and television shows) to come back home to Boonetown and place his hands and feet into the concrete. Unfortunately, it was all rather anti-climactic.

You see, there was only one other local man who had become famous and appeared in movies and on television, and he, sadly, had already passed away. And Daniel Boone was long gone. Nana would have been another logical choice, since she had appeared on Johnny Carson, but apparently, she was never considered. So, all hopes for a Walk of Stars sort of ended there, with that one square out in front of the theater. Let's just say the Boonetown Walk of Stars was a short walk. I'm glad they centered his square, because otherwise it might have looked really odd to have this one set of hand and foot prints just randomly there in the sidewalk. But at least this way he doesn't have to compete with anyone else: He has the sidewalk all to himself. Even now, he's still there, all alone, waiting for Boonetown to spawn another celebrity to keep him company.

This is what I mean about making do. And even though our Walk of Stars is brief, you never have to worry about crowds.

I think it was Christmas before last when the City of Boonetown and a local club went in together to bring an ice-skating rink to Boonetown. This was of great interest to me because I love watching figure skating on television and have always been sad that we never had a skating rink. I'm sure with proper training I would have been at the Olympics, knocking out triple axels. But alas, no local rink was to be found. Actually, in the South, ice-skating rinks are very scarce. Yet here was the announcement. The paper said, that this new skating rink was going to be outdoors and downtown on the square. What? I thought, how is that possible?

They kept on teasing it every week in the paper. Then it was revealed that the rink would only be there for a weekend. I knew something was up. There was no way anyone would build a rink with real ice for just a couple of days. And what about weather? It's usually warm in Tennessee in December.

As time got closer, we learned that the city and the club had to pay twenty-thousand dollars to get the rink for the weekend. They insisted that the money made on rentals and admissions would more that cover the cost of the rink, and it would bring the masses to the downtown square. I was still concerned because now I knew it had to be fake, or some sort of simulated ice surface. Then I saw where they were going to put it: Just on a small corner of a downtown parking lot.

I was even more skeptical.

Turns out, the visions of a weekend filled with kids and parents holding hands, gliding around the ice in downtown Boonetown, were as unrealistic as I thought.

The ice rink turned out to be a bunch of big thick sheets of plastic they had laid down on the parking lot surface. Since no one in town knew how to skate anyway, I guess they weren't as disappointed with the surface as you might think. I never saw any gliding, or axel jumps, or spins. It was a pretty sad display overall: a lot of people in ice skates, taking lots of selfies, basically walking around on a big sheet of plastic in a parking lot on a sixty-degree day.

Thankfully, it got more festive at night. They had lots of twinkling lights so it was harder to tell that no one was gliding in skates over the plastic rink, mostly just pushing the skates over the surface and trying not to get stuck in the plastic and trip.

Later in the evening, some of the kids discovered if they removed their skates, they could actually glide over the simulated ice in their sock feet. So, the kids did get to glide, but they could also do the same thing at home on their hardwood floors. It was hard to see the point of the whole thing.

I suppose with good editing, you could get some video of the children appearing to ice skate, even if they were sans skates. In the end, it wasn't really a Norman Rockwell scene, I'd say more like Chevy Chase from *Christmas Vacation*. Still, it was a time to get the family together.

And, as I said before, in a small town, sometimes you just have to make do.

Taxi Driver

"Where you going?" the taxi driver said, as I got into the back of the cab at the Nashville Airport.

Well, actually, he said something I couldn't really understand. But considering he was driving me and needed direction, I deduced that was probably what he meant. He had a strong accent.

"University Square Condominiums on 19th Avenue South. Do you know where it is?" I ask.

Confused look from Taxi Driver. "Uhhh, I think so," he says.

"If you can just get me to the Demonbreun exit," I say, "I can show you from there."

"Aaaaahhhh Deemumbrm! Aaahhh, yes, aaahh yesssss, know it! Aaaahhhh, high-five, high-fiveeee-eeeehhh" he said extending his hand in the air.

I reluctantly high-five him. I can say with a reasonable level certainty that this is the first time I have high-fived my taxi driver.

He told me he was from Somalia and said "Have you ever been to Africa?"

"No, I haven't" I said.

I'm always amazed by people who can move to a new country and assimilate so quickly. Yes, he had a strong accent, but English was his second language. I had just been to New York and my southern accent is always a topic of discussion there. And I can only speak one language.

He said he had lived in the US for about eleven years. Then, while looking straight back at me (and without any noticeable concern for the road) he proceeded to barrage me with about one hundred questions. "You married? Where you work? What you do? You from Nashville? Where you born? Here? Where you live, house or apartment? How old you are?"

"Forty-eight" I say.

"You no look that old," he says. He was thirty-five-ish, very thin and VERY friendly.

"Are you German?" he says.

"No," I say, "I mean, yes, I am from German ancestry." I am wondering how he knows this. Do I look *that* German? (I was thinking he has to be very observant to be able to identify ethnic backgrounds.)

I was longing for those wonderful impersonal cab rides I, too often, take for granted in New York City, where there is thick, bullet-proof glass between you and the driver, and the driver is listening to an i-pod and never speaks. You are not even completely sure if he speaks English. The only words spoken are when you ask how much you owe.

But this guy, driving slower and slower so he could ask more questions, was relentless. He hit me with so many questions so fast, I couldn't remember them and could barely get them answered. (At some point in the conversation we had to high-five again because I got a question right.) Eventually, I pretended to text on my phone hoping that would shut him up, but that only brought on more questions. "Is that an iPhone? Who's your carrier?" he says.

"Yes, Verizon," I say.

"Ahhh, I have t-muble" he says.

If he was working on his tip, he wasn't succeeding, especially when he asked me if I played "biscuit-ball". I did tell him that because of my height I was constantly asked if I played basketball, and I did not.

"Why not?" he says.

No response from me.

Then out of the clear blue sky he starts this new thing. He says, "I see you have chicky-legs so I thought you play biscuit-ball."

"What?" I said.

"Chicky-legs," he says again. "You have chicky-legs, I thought you play biscuit-ball."

I wanted to say that chicky-legs are hereditary and no amount of squats will change that. But I knew that was just too high a mountain to climb with his accent and my level of irritation. "What about *his* chicky-legs?" I was thinking. They are skinnier than mine. And how did he even get a good look at my chicky-legs? I was wearing shorts, but I got in the cab so fast I didn't see how he even noticed anything about me.

Maybe he was just hungry and was really talking about Kentucky Fried Chicken. Maybe I had jumped to conclusions since I really was having trouble understanding him. I wasn't completely sure.

But he kept looking back at my legs.

I couldn't stiff him on the tip with a clear conscience. I mean my legs are skinny, but I am six-foot-six, for God's sake. It was just a few years ago that I got to the point that I could wear shorts in public without feeling self-conscious. I didn't need this kind of setback.

I was hoping he would speed up, but no, he was enjoying our leisurely Sunday afternoon chat way too much. I began to point out the turns to him since I was convinced he had no idea where he was going. A few high-fives and about twenty questions later, we arrived at my building. I was exhausted.

I have a feeling me and my chicky-legs will drive to the airport next time.

And Sew It Goes

I keep a clear glass jar full of buttons on a shelf in my living room. These are buttons from four generations.

When my grandmother passed away, there was a big box of buttons in her attic. The buttons were going to be thrown out, but I knew I needed to keep them. It was a treasure trove of buttons... every shape, color and size. The box contained not only my grandmother's buttons, but my great-grandmother's collection of extra buttons, too. Back then, everyone that sewed kept their extra buttons handy for making repairs to garments that had lost a button.

When my mother died, I added her buttons to my collection. She was keeping her spare buttons in the fishbowl I got when I won a goldfish at the Boone County Fair. Looking at that colorful display in the clear bowl, I decided it would be a perfect way to display all these buttons, now including my extra buttons.

My mother told me that my great-grandmother was a tailor who made wedding gowns and men's suits. I can only imagine how difficult it would be to make a man's suit from scratch. That is something that neither I nor my mother ever attempted. (Although, once, in that harrowing period of fashion called the seventies, she did make me that leisure suit.) Mom never attempted a wedding gown either, though she did make many formals for my sister.

When my grandma married my grandfather, the newlyweds moved to the country to live on a farm. Grandma was a short woman with a wonderful outlook on life, and her groom was very tall and kind of brooding.

I can't recall Grandma making clothes, although I'm sure she probably made dresses for my mother and my aunt. Her sewing efforts were very utilitarian and at the same time extremely creative: she was a quilter. I have no idea how many quilts she made over the years. Based on how many quilt-tops I saw her working on and how many were on beds and stored in trunks, there had to be close to a hundred.

It's hard to comprehend how she was able to complete them. She was the mother six children, had a garden, and had a henhouse where she collected eggs every morning and then sold them by the dozen to supplement their income. Every morning she made my grandpa a fresh cobbler and the cats a skillet of cornbread. Both of them were gone by the end of the day.

In the afternoon, she would sit in front of the TV and watch her stories, (daytime soap operas) and quilt. She believed the stories were real and would often call my mother or I and express her concern about Doug and Julie on *Days of our Lives*. She thought they were reality shows before reality shows existed.

Her quilt squares were filled with colorful fabrics in various shapes, working together to form baskets and stars and rings and other designs. Her sweet manner and joyful outlook on life were on full display in her quilt tops.

I guess creative sewing is just part of my heritage.

My earliest childhood recollection is of me sitting on the floor under the sewing machine while my mother was sewing. I could not have been older than four or five at the time. After sufficient begging, my mother would give me a needle and thread and some scraps of fabric and I would begin stitching them together. At the time I was just mimicking what I had seen her do and I'm sure I had no idea what I was making. But I loved the process of sewing two pieces of fabric together.

I quickly learned to sew on buttons, sew a seam, and put in a hem. By the time I got to the first grade, I could make some pretty primitive clothing. Don't ask me about the quality of these garments: it wasn't good. However, I do remember that they were quite unique.

My mother didn't encourage me to sew because (I think) she thought I was missing out on all the fun the neighborhood boys were having playing ball, riding bikes, and such. But those activities weren't creative. I was always watching and studying what she was doing and I was learning a skill that would serve me the rest of my life.

Of course, there was a downside to all this creativity. The boys in the neighborhood would beat me up and call me a sissy because I liked to sew.

But that didn't stop me.

One problem I did have was that I was very impatient (I still am) and I always wanted to rush and get finished quickly. Mom would always try to get me to slow down and use proper technique. (I am glad she did. Even though I am still always in a hurry to finish, I do know the right way to do things when I want to do a really good job.) Unlike me, my sister had a lot of patience. She became an excellent seamstress and she loved to do hand embroidery. She was also a perfectionist which came in handy as she made all kinds of beautiful embroidered pieces that hung throughout our home.

Mom had told me about a girl she went to high school with named Ann, who always did messy work, but at the last minute would take an iron and press out all of the flaws. It made Mom mad that Ann could do such sloppy work and then magically press it all out. I remember once, being in the middle of one of my frenzied projects. I was not using proper technique, just sewing as fast as I could to get something done. Mom told me that I reminded her of Ann. I knew instantly what she meant. Ann, like I, was probably jealous of Mom's expert skills and patience, and I think maybe Mom was a little jealous of my free-form style.

I was doing some fairly advanced sewing at a pretty young age. When I was twelve I was really excited to move into my own room in our basement. It wasn't fancy, but it was mine to decorate as I pleased. I found some striped fabric in my mom's fabric chest. I decided I would make some Roman shades for my window like the ones Rhoda had in her New York apartment. On the television show *Rhoda* that is. It was a popular television series in the seventies, and she had a cool New York apartment. (My favorite television apartment was Mary Richard's Minneapolis apartment — the second one — in the high rise. But Mary had a skyline view and gorgeous furniture that I could not possibly duplicate in my basement room, so I decided I would be better off to use Rhoda's eclectic

New York apartment for inspiration.)

I had no idea how to make Roman shades. But I had kite string and had found some little white rings in Mom's sewing box, and I took coat hangers and unfolded them to make the frame. It took me a while to figure out how to make them with these limited supplies. But when I finished, I had some real, operating, Roman shades. My mom had the strangest look on her face when I showed her how I could raise and lower them. I think she was both shocked and amazed.

In my teen years, Mom began to trust my design instincts more because I think she realized I could *see* things, in my mind. I call it my movie screen: right above my eyebrows, but on the inside. Since I was able do this, I mistakenly thought that everyone had the gift of visualization. However, when I began working on design projects with others, it became obvious that they did not.

When my mom would be shopping for fabric, she would buy a pattern she liked, but would only choose a fabric that looked like the fabric in the illustration on the pattern. I would suggest other fabrics. She would say she could not see it. I just thought she was being stubborn, but after a while I realized that she really *could not* see it. I could. I could see any fabric in the store made up in any pattern in the catalog. So, I instantly knew which fabrics would look good in a certain style and which would look bad.

Even now, it's the same on my interior design projects. I can see a completed room, in any color or style, in my mind. I can change the colors, or the furniture, with just a quick thought. At first, when I would describe a room to a client and show them fabric samples, I would get blank stares. Once again, I just assumed they could visualize, but the blank stare said otherwise.

That's when I learned to sketch the rooms for my clients. If I could help them see the room, then they were so much more confident in my design plans for their den or kitchen or whole house.

After I bought my own home at age twenty-one. I would make all my own window treatments, throw pillows, slipcovers and anything else I needed. I even learned to make some furniture. I would make a wood form for an ottoman and then upholster it. I also made lots of upholstered headboards, I even ended up selling some of them.

Sometimes, if I had a big project, I would still go out to Mom's big sewing room to work. She would always help, too, and it was nice to have someone to talk to while I was working. We had a lot of laughs working in that room.

The last few years of my mother's life she didn't do much sewing. She had cancer and was unable to be as productive as she had been in her heyday. She still would do the occasional repair or alteration for my dad, but that was about all.

I remember one day when I visited, I noticed that she had gone through the sewing room and straightened-up and organized everything in a way that she had not done before. I think she knew it was the last time she would straighten her sewing room and wanted to leave things in good order. It was incredibly sad to see that place looking neat and orderly. As much as I hate messes, our creations came from those messes. So they were a welcome sight in the sewing room. But that day there were no sewing projects in progress. The room was tidy, and it was a bleak omen. Seeing the sewing machine put away in its cabinet was almost like a burial.

When Mother died, I kept her sewing machine. I

have it in storage. I just couldn't stand the idea of someone else having her sewing machine, or worse yet, it ending up in a landfill. It had bonded the two of us, and I couldn't let it go.

When my sister and I were clearing out the house, I found some of my childhood clothes in Mom's attic. Some she had made for me and some she had adapted to fit my long arms and legs. It reminded me how much of my childhood had been spent with my mother in that sewing room, and how many good, and a few bad, experiments were conducted in our attempts to create something for me or for her.

Over the last few years, many of my friends (the ones that know how much I enjoy design) have urged me to try out for *Project Runway.* I had never told them about my secret desire to do it. I have always designed clothes in my mind and always wanted to be a fashion designer. But growing up in a small town in the South, it just never seemed to be an option for me and now, as I look toward my fifty-eighth birthday, I feel a bit overwhelmed by the thought of such a daunting challenge. But my friends thought I could really do well.

And I know my friends would be rooting for me. I think it would be ironic if my employees (I own a construction business now) gathered to watch me on *Project Runway* like they do to watch a pro football game. These tough guys, taking a day off from deer hunting, discussing the pros and cons of the evening gown I created out of plastic tablecloths (or whatever the crazy challenge). That alone would almost be worth me entering.

Still, Project Runway is not likely in my future. Oh, I know the designs in my head might be good enough. But as luck would have it, along with that talent for sewing, I have also inherited arthritis from my grandmother. Sitting bent over a sewing machine, ironically, is one thing that really inflames the arthritis in my back. So, I guess any sewing I do will be for my own satisfaction and not for a TV show competition.

I think Mom would be happy that I still use so many of the techniques she taught me and that I do try to slow down and do a better job. I'm still terribly impatient, but I find I enjoy the process more these days. I've taught a couple of friends to sew recently, and I loved the experience of sharing what I know.

I occasionally catch myself looking over at that glass bowl of buttons on my bookshelf and wonder if they might ever mean as much to their next caretaker. But I know they won't. How could they?

They are part of a story that ends with me. And that's ok.

I'll keep throwing my extra buttons in that big glass bowl, though, and remember all those wonderful creations.

One of the Guys

The summer I turned fourteen, I began working the office front desk at my father's sheet metal and roofing business. This would have been in 1976 or thereabouts. It was mainly clerical work, plus waiting on customers and answering the phone. Because I was more the artsy type, I fit in better in the office than out in the shop, but to say I "fit" in at all was a big stretch.

The men in the shop didn't really know what to think of me. They were nice to me, mainly because I was the boss's son, I think. I guess I did stick out like a sore thumb. They were all in their work clothes, but since I was in the office, I was usually in an Izod sweater, khaki pants and Bass loafers. Technically I was in business casual, but no one else in the office was. They all wore jeans. My appearance was a big deal to me, but I don't think clothes were much of a concern for anyone else working there. A few of the guys seemed to like me, and they *loved* to talk. I covered the office by myself during lunch and I would often get an earful from the guys in the shop.

My dad had started the business when he returned

home from the Air Force. The business was successful. The sheet metal shop mainly produced duct work for the heating and air conditioning systems he installed. He also installed roofing and he had a KitchenAid dishwasher dealership long before KitchenAid became the name brand it is today. This was before everyone had a dishwasher, so he installed a lot of them. (I'm not sure how that came about because it had nothing to do with roofing or air conditioning.) The sheet metal shop also stocked gutter and stove pipe. Stove pipes were used to vent the smoke from old fashioned wood stoves into the flue of the rural homes that still heated with wood. The nearby Amish community still primarily heated that way, and a lot of other folks in the area had put wood stoves in their homes as a source of cheap heat during the energy crisis of the seventies. Dad carried just about anything he thought might sell. Occasionally, he still had to wait on customers.

All through my childhood, I heard my dad tell this one story and, in retrospect, I guess maybe it was a lesson in how to get out of a tricky situation with a customer. It worked for him, but it would have never worked for me. All in the delivery, I think. But it's still worth telling.

Every afternoon at four, the shop closed and my dad and a couple of his friends would have a drink before heading home. They did not like to be interrupted once they sat down with a scotch. On this particular day, a customer ignored the closed sign and came right in my dad's office asking for a half a stick of stove pipe. (I know these are technical terms, so bear with me. A stick of stove pipe is a four-foot long piece of round pipe and a half a stick is a two-foot long piece.) Begrudgingly, my dad went out to the shop and found one of the guys packing up to leave.

Dad yelled over to him, "Hey, some son-of-a-bitch up front wants a half a stick of stove pipe, can you get that for me?"

At which time, my dad turned around and found that the customer had followed him into the shop and was standing behind him. Without missing a beat, my dad turned back to the worker and said, "and this nice gentleman would like the other half." Dad was quick.

I knew I'd never be able to charm customers like my dad, but I learned a lot by observing him. There wasn't any training program, it was just trial and error. After a few summers of working the counter during my high school years, I had learned a lot about the business, but I was also getting a lot of other lessons too, many I didn't really want. Lunch was when everyone was gone, except for me and one shop man, Larryalan Wopp, who worked during the lunch hour to fill any shop orders.

Larryalan chain-smoked, always had on a torn white t-shirt with a lot of grease and oil stains, and had a big plump round stomach that made it hard for him to keep his pants up. Every step he took was followed by a tug up on his waist band.

When we weren't busy, Larryalan would prop up on the counter in front of my desk (there was air conditioning there) and spill all the details of his personal life.

Not that I ever asked. Lord knows, I didn't want to know the details. But he shared freely and openly.

Larryalan was a twin. His brother, Harryalan Wopp, was in prison for murder (or attempted murder, I can't recall). Larryalan said that Harryalan was the black sheep of the family since he was in state prison. Larryalan proudly stated that he had only done prison-time locally, making him the white sheep of the family (I supposed).

One day, Larryalan's wife stopped by to pick up his check which prompted Larryalan to tell me about how they met. I guess every couple has that sweet first-meeting story, and he did too.

It seems Larryalan had been arrested on some "trumped up" child abuse charges that he said his old lady had made up because she was mad at him. (The fact that we were talking about prison time and child abuse charges made me pause and question my dad's hiring policies.) Larryalan continued the story saying that from his holding cell, he first saw Linda, coming into the sheriff's office. She had stopped in to press charges against her old man for beating her up... again.

Larryalan said, "She had two black eyes and tight blue jeans and damn she was sexy." He went on to say, "I knew she was the one right then."

My fourteen-year-old self briefly thought there was a country music song in there somewhere...two black eyes, tight blue jeans, in she walked, the woman of my dreams. It did rhyme, but then it occurred to me that Larryalan would likely be the only person to find black eyes sexy. So the target audience would be quite limited.

Well, Linda indeed was the right one. They ended up living together and eventually married. He said at first, they lived together "plasonically" (I think he meant platonically) before they married. Even at fourteen I was skeptical of the truth of that. Maybe he thought I would judge.

Linda was a character herself. The fact that she said she was a practicing Witch didn't bother me too much since she assured me, when we first met, that she liked me and would not cast any spells on me. I felt like there was a veiled threat in there somewhere, but since I didn't believe in witchcraft, I didn't spend a lot of time on it. Linda had long, dark, stringy black hair and chain-smoked as well, so, as far as I was concerned, she looked the part.

Over those summers, I worked the counter with Larryalan as my sidekick. He continued to freely share the intimate details of their private life. In time, it all became old hat and I forgot most of the details. But...

There was one episode I filed away in the back of my mind. Or should I say it was burned there. I will warn you in advance it falls squarely under the heading of "too much information."

One day, Larryalan was moving slowly and said he had been suffering dreadfully...with hemorrhoids. Now, in all my life, I have never felt it necessary to share they details of a bad cold or even a wrenching stomach virus, but not Larryalan. He pressed on. He had been to the doctor that morning and was prescribed some salve, as he called it. So, the next day, he said that Linda had applied the salve to the affected area. (Why he had not done this himself is still a mystery.)

He said, "As soft as her hands were, they still felt like sandpaper. Even laying spread eagle in front of the fan in the open window didn't help."

Hope the neighbors weren't out on the patio that evening.

Larryalan also loved to give me all the dirt on the other employees. I was always amazed at how jealous the wives were about their husbands that worked in the shop. Back then, most of Dad's employees were hard working, middle-aged men, unconcerned about their appearance. I didn't think any of the wives had much to worry about.

For sure, not Odell Green's wife. But Mrs. Green

was jealous to the extreme.

According to Larryalan, Odell had been sleeping in the camper on the back of his pickup truck for a few weeks, since his wife had been threatening to kill him in his sleep. His wife was convinced he was having an affair. Odell was a fifty-something, unpleasant sort, who did meticulous work, but was quiet and didn't seem to be the type to have an affair.

At the time, I already knew about the affair accusations since I answered the phone in the office. Mrs. Green usually called during lunch when Odell and some of the other men were up at Jack's having a hamburger. I'd answer, and she would always have the same questions, and I would follow with the same responses:

"No, he's gone to lunch...Well, I saw him walking toward Jack's but beyond that, I can't say where he's at...I don't know if he's meeting a woman at Jack's...I really don't know if he's having an affair. That's something you should discuss with him...Yes, I'll give him a message."

It always amazed me that she would make me read back her message. You would think hearing her death threats read aloud might jolt her a bit and make her re-evaluate, but not in this case. She seemed to delight in it.

"Yes, I'll read it back: Your wife knows all about you and that—"

I'm thinking to myself is that w-h-o-r-e, or h-o-a-r? We didn't go over that one in spelling at Holy Rosary Catholic School so I chose the first.

"—whore you have been fooling around with. If you don't quit seeing that whore, I'm going to shoot you in your sleep."

"Yes, I got it...Yes, I'll give it to him...Yes, I

included the part about killing him...Yes, I know you have a gun."

Blah Blah Blah: death threats, ailments, romance. Same thing every day at lunch.

I was finding clerical work so tedious.

It's All In the Design

I've always been pretty sure I would die in some type of freak interior design accident.

Like the time I was moving a large, heavy, antique, pine armoire to my basement. I had the idea that I could just get behind it, and slide it down the stairs ever-so gently, and then stop it, ever-so gently, on the landing in the basement.

The plan was flawed.

The armoire ended up on top of me. While stuck with knotty pine an inch from my face, I was debating how long it would be before someone would come looking for me and what state of decay my body might be in when they eventually did find me. I didn't have a cell phone on me, and the armoire was sort of wedged in the stairwell above me.

You might wonder why I didn't enlist trained movers, but the reason I didn't illustrates a lifelong problem. I am *not* patient. Especially when working on a design project.

I want to see the finished project and I want to see it right now. I don't want to wait on the painters to put on the final coat, or the electricians to do the final bit of wiring. I want to put on the finishing touches and I want to take pictures. So, when I needed to get the armoire out of my living room and into my basement, I wanted it done that night.

And so there I was, trapped under it, preparing for death. I suddenly became very concerned about my obituary photo. In the *Boonetown Times*, I mean. Years ago, no one put photos of the deceased in the paper, but now it seems to be a requirement. And there is simply no explaining some of them. I was hoping that someone had possession of a good recent photo of me.

In a pinch, I've seen some families take a photo of the deceased in the casket and put it with the obit. It's also common to use a high school senior photo for folks in their eighties and nineties. I know it was a good picture, maybe even Granny's favorite, but maybe not very accurate. Then, there is always one with the person in a hospital bed and oxygen tubes in their nose. It's obviously the last picture to be taken of this person. Couldn't they just take out the tubes for a second?

Last week there was one from the "Glamor Shots" era. Remember those? Women would go in and be dressed to look glamorous, I suppose, but often they just looked a bit trashy. This obit was for an eighty-year old woman (probably about fifty-five in the photo) with highly-teased, frosted hair, wearing a cowboy hat propped lightly atop her 'do. She was holding a pistol and blowing on the barrel as if to indicate she had just shot an unfaithful lover. I couldn't help but wonder if she looked at the proofs from that photo shoot and thought, YES, this one will be perfect for my obituary.

I felt very relieved that I had never gone in for any glamor shots, but was also concerned about what my family might choose. Surely not my senior picture. I hated it.

While I was laying under there, I started thinking about what got me to this point in life. I was a professional interior designer. Not exactly full-time, but I was doing a lot of it, in combination with my full-time job. Really, the "professional" part started off accidentally. Friends would see what I was doing to my own house and then would ask me to work on their house. But my being intrigued with interior design when back even farther. When I tell people my love of interior design started young, I mean it.

I had this neighbor lady who lived next door and she was quite a bit older than my parents. When I was six or seven, she would invite me over for tea after school. Hot tea, not iced tea. Very English. She was very much into decorating and was always buying something for her house. She had the first loveseat in the neighborhood and I thought that was pretty cool. I'd always help her husband get their Christmas decorations down from the attic, and then help him put them up. I loved any kind of decorating. But my mom never wanted to spend any money on new furniture or décor. (Probably had something to do with the fact that I outgrew my clothes about three times a year, but was that really my fault?)

My neighbor was a total hypochondriac, and she was constantly talking about her heath ailments. I could put up with that because she had subscriptions to *Better Homes and Gardens* and *House Beautiful*. We didn't. Now before you say I was just using her for her magazines, that's not completely true, I did enjoy her company. But to me, back then, a good home design magazine was like porn and I had to feed my addiction for the latest design trends.

I was redecorating my room on a regular basis by the time I was thirteen. I had convinced my mom and dad to let me move into the basement: my brother and I shared a room and we could not get along. He was more Allman Brothers and I was more Barry Manilow, and those issues alone were reason enough for us to live apart.

One day, my dad had a carpenter come to our house and build two walls in the corner of the basement and suddenly I had a room of my own. My brother was convinced I'd be scared to stay down there myself, but I was so glad to get away from him. I was never afraid.

I would scrounge up any piece of furniture I could find around the house or at my dad's office or wherever and use my allowance or yard-mowing money to buy a can of spray paint, and then paint a table or a chest, or do some sort of art project, and update my room.

In college, I had ended up getting a business degree. I thought that would be more appropriate for what I would be doing in the family business and more marketable in general, but my first love was always design. After college, in my early twenties, I bought and renovated my first home. I guess word got around that I had good ideas because people began asking me to do design work. I never solicited it. In Boonetown, I didn't know of any working designers, and it was hard for me to imagine making a living in that field (there was no internet back then). All my jobs were referred through word of mouth or repeat clients. I never wanted to feel like I was forcing my ideas on anyone, so it worked a lot better for me if I just let people approach me. I loved that people were asking me to help them with their own homes.

Some jobs got off to a rough start.

Once I brought drawings over to a client's home and was sitting on the sofa between the husband and the wife. They were considering an addition. The wife was engaged in my presentation, but the husband seemed to be either awestruck by my sketches, or appalled at my lack of talent, because he had nothing to say and a completely blank stare.

Thankfully, before he completely lost consciousness, I noticed that one of my canoe-size shoes was pressing firmly on the oxygen hose that was running from the tank, across the front of the sofa, and up into his nose. He was neither awed nor appalled: He was simply oxygen-deprived and trying not to gasp for breath in front of me. He was a real southern gentlemen. Apparently, he did like the sketches, because when his brain became active again, I did do the addition to their home and it turned out quite well.

I found that I loved being creative and developing my design skills, more than I ever imagined. One of the best benefits was that many of my clients became wonderful friends. One of my first clients ended up being one I have worked with the longest. I've done every room in her house—more than once—and I've designed two additions for her as well. It's been a thirty-plus-year collaboration.

Another client was a widower who I had known before I worked on his house. But after working on the project, we ended up being great friends. When I finished the house, he said, "The design you created for my home is exactly what I would have done if I had known how." In my business, I think that's about the best compliment you can get.

I've always loved old homes. I've built a new home, and designed a few for clients, but it's pretty much impossible to duplicate the character that exists in a hundred-year-old house.

When I was fifteen, my parents began planning a

new home. I was so excited. I was ready to move, too. But I didn't want them to build a new home. I had other ideas.

I had seen an ad in the *Boonetown Times* for a house that was being sold for seventy-nine thousand dollars. This was an unbelievable deal on a wonderful old house. It was on a great big tree-filled lot, in an excellent location. The very large, old, two-story Georgian-style brick wreaked of class. I *begged* my parents to go look at that house.

No deal. Dad wanted to build. I begged more. No way. I told him more than once about all the potential it had. Still, no deal. I was only fifteen and he would not listen. I was so disappointed. I spent a lot of time imagining what I could do with that house.

Eventually, a young couple ended up buying that house, and Dad decided we would build a new house on the other side of town. I was very involved in the process, but, as with most new houses, it was lacking in character. I never thought it felt like home.

Luckily, fate stepped in and helped out.

It took a while, but years later, (actually a couple of decades later), I ended up working on that house. A friend of mine recommended me to the owner, Sarah. Sarah's husband had died at a young age of cancer, and she was a widow with three daughters. She wanted to update the house and I was really excited to get the chance to work on it. We immediately clicked. Not only did we have many fun adventures as we accumulated things for the house, we ended up becoming great friends, too.

During the process of redecorating that great old house, we would make these all-day trips to Nashville to shop. Boonetown had very limited options on the décor front. In Nashville, we would usually make a visit to the fabric stores and the rug store down on Second Avenue. (This was before Nashville became hip and all those places were forced out.) Then we would make our way to a couple of furniture stores, and almost always stop by City Lighting.

Sarah and I were on our way to City Lighting one day, discussing what kind of mood we might find the owners in. If you ever shopped there, you know.

City Lighting had a fantastic selection of lamps and lamp shades. It was run by a husband and wife, Uri and Elaine, and you could often feel the tension in the air when you went in. Sometimes the tension was between them and a customer, and other times it was just between the two of them.

They did not like children in the store. At all. They had lots of lamps sitting on the floor, and I know they were concerned about lamps being damaged and children being injured. Signs would inform you that children were not allowed to roam around or run though the store. When someone walked in with children, they got a complimentary warning.

Then, if the children did run around, you would get a second stern warning in a huffy tone from Uri. Something like, "Please keep your children under control." This was accompanied by a side-eye glance from Elaine and a glare from Uri.

I was in the store only a couple of times when one of those "third warnings" was given out. They were always some version of Uri screaming and pointing at the offender, "Take your children and get out of my store this minute and don't come back!"

I am not exaggerating.

City Lighting had rules. They told you the rules up front, but still, people messed up. One day, I drove up and Uri was out on the sidewalk stomping on a brand-new lampshade as hard as he could. The one BIG rule was this: Never, *ever*, return a lampshade if you have removed the plastic.

All the lampshades come wrapped in plastic to protect them from stains and damage. City Lighting's policy was simple. You could return a lampshade within three days if you didn't like it, *only* if the plastic was in-tact. If you had removed the plastic, watch out.

As I went in the store that day, I walked by Uri (he didn't notice me, he was busy), while a lady was arguing with Elaine at the counter. One of the other customers filled me in. It was just as I had expected. The Lady brought back a shade and had removed the plastic. Uri had told her he would not give her a refund and she protested. An argument ensued. Uri had yelled "I will take this lampshade out on the sidewalk and stomp it flat before I give you a refund!"

He was obviously doing just that when I drove up.

One of the last times I was in the store, before they closed down and moved, you could cut the tension with a knife. Elaine was giving him cutting looks, as she did so well, and he was in an obvious huff. Every time they passed each other, there were words. I could tell things were coming to a head and was trying to get my business done and get out. Right before he checked me out, she said something and he blew.

"All right, that's it! Everyone out of the store, right now!" he yelled.

I was like the other customers: stunned. Not wanting to press our luck, we all went out to the front sidewalk. The screaming and yelling could be heard into the parking lot. I felt like I should leave because it seemed like it might go on a while, but I needed the lamps to finish a job and didn't want to make another trip. I decided to wait it out.

Sure enough, a few minutes later, he came to the door and invited us back in.

I think he said something like "We just had a little matter that needed to be ironed out."

I really miss City Lighting. Shopping there was more of an adventure than a chore. I always wondered if their business model included the concepts like, "Let's keep our customers on edge," or "We hold nothing in." Uri and Elaine were always somewhat friendly to me, since I was a good customer (I could never count all the lamps I bought there over the years), but I always knew I was walking a fine line, and things could turn on a dime.

On one particular morning, the local Nashville radio stations had been warning that the weather forecast included possible tornadoes. But in Tennessee, in the spring, that was the forecast most every day. So, Sarah and I headed out to Nashville not too worried, and too busy talking to listen to the radio. Turns out this was not a good plan. We weren't too far from City Lights when things took a turn.

At the intersection of Broadway and West End Avenue, facing downtown Nashville, we felt the wind pick up and pick up quickly. As a matter of fact, it began to literally pick us up. The rear end of my car was being lifted off the ground by massive gusts of wind. We were in six lanes of bumper-to-bumper traffic at a red light and everyone had just stopped. There was nowhere to go. The car would rise and then fall back to the ground. Thankfully, we never went airborne.

We both looked at each other and simultaneously said, "We are about to die."

Sarah said, "Thank God I didn't go on that diet,

maybe that's what's holding us down."

I laughed, but I was sure grateful Sarah had been over-eating.

In the distance, we could see the dark-gray funnel cloud hovering over downtown Nashville, and we watched it move across the skyline. It looked like it was happening on a big movie screen in front of us. The roof of a building would start to peel up from one side and then proceed to peel across the entire building. Once the roof would get to about a forty-five-degree angle, it would just explode into a million bits of debris. As my car was doing the hop, skip, and jump on the pavement, we saw roofs explode over several buildings. People were jumping out of cars and running toward buildings, and some were driving over the sidewalk into the parking lots nearby. It felt like the tornado was heading our way since debris was flying through the air around us. As soon as I could find a clear path, I drove across the street into the Beaman Used Car lot. I may have landed in a handicap spot, but there wasn't really time to assess.

I kind of thought we should stay in the car, since a lot of stuff was airborne, but before I could voice that thought, Sarah had jumped out and was running toward a little office building. I was not at all confident about this choice, since the office building was basically an all-glass trailer sitting on some stilts in a parking lot. I decided to follow her.

We ran through the office looking for any room without windows. When we finally found one, we thought it was empty until we noticed the desk had about ten pairs of legs sticking out from under it. We had located the entire sales staff.

We kind of crouched down behind all of them. I'm not sure why because by this time the tornado had passed over, but it still seemed like the right thing to do. We stayed there for a while, probably thirty minutes or so, and listened to the radio until the weatherman said it had cleared the area. But we also heard that the interstates were closed. Still, I thought we could get out by heading away from downtown (where the tornado had touched down) and go toward Green Hills. From there, I figured we could take the old highway and head south to Boonetown.

By the time we got to the Green Hills area, the news reported another tornado had been spotted and was heading directly toward Green Hills.

The safest and closest place I could think of was the parking garage at the Green Hills Mall, so I turned in there. We decided to go in the mall and wait out the tornado inside. But no sooner than we walked in the door, sirens began going off. We were ushered into one of the concrete-block halls behind the stores for our own safety. We met a lot of other customers who had been stuck there too, for safe keeping, and we all ended up having to stay there about an hour.

The more news we heard, the worse things sounded. There were multiple tornadoes converging on various parts of Nashville and middle Tennessee.

We weren't sure what to do, but in a case like this, it seems the natural inclination is to try to get home. We were listening closely to the radio and monitoring the weather. After things were clear in Green Hills, we decided to start making our way south. Nothing seemed to be going on in that area and we knew getting home was going to be a long process. In other areas, tornados were still popping up everywhere. Our cell service was out, so we couldn't let people know where we were.

We pulled over once, in Franklin, after being told to take cover, but never saw anything near us, so we decided to keep moving slowly toward home. We had not eaten all day and were beginning to get hungry as we continued south into the Spring Hill area. And of course, once again as if on cue, the weatherman said a tornado was heading straight for Spring Hill.

There was an old concrete block diner right there on the highway. It looked sturdy, so we decided to take cover there, thinking we could also get something to eat. (Sarah was badly in need of coffee too.) We were getting pretty weary of the whole "take cover" thing, but decided if we were going to get blown away, maybe it would be best to have a full stomach.

Being safety-minded, we did ask for a table in the back, away from the windows. We were stunned to find out that many of the patrons hadn't even heard about the weather and all the tornadoes. They just were enjoying a meal. It was late afternoon by now and tornadoes were ravaging the mid-state, but the diners there seemed oblivious.

We must have stayed there another hour or so, waiting to see if the weather looked clear toward home. Even though our nerves were a bit frazzled, we were glad to get back on the road, especially since our family members had not heard from us.

I guess it was around six when we got close to Boonetown. We were stopped about fifteen miles north of town. Another tornado had ripped through the area and crossed the highway taking out telephone poles and trees.

By the time we made it to my house, Sarah and I were chastised by some of our family members for stopping to eat when they were worried sick about us. In my frazzled state, I reminded them that, had I not ordered the coconut pie, we might have driven right into that tornado north of town, and that telephone pole we saw laying across the highway could have fallen right on us. So, the dessert, in retrospect, was a life-saving move. This is not the first time in my life I have felt that coconut cream pie had lifesaving qualities.

Turns out that day was a historic weather day. More tornados hit the Middle Tennessee area in one day than in recorded history. Nashville had massive amounts of damage. We were right in the middle of it. Thankfully we got home safely. We weren't smart that day, by any means, just lucky.

Years later, Sarah decided that her house (the one we almost died trying to decorate in a tornado) was too large for her. She moved to a smaller place just across the street and passed the big house along to her daughter. Her daughter hired me to do an even more extensive renovation, adding a new kitchen and a master bath. I ended up getting to redo that house not once, but twice.

I joke about getting killed on a design job and I guess that could happen someday. But the truth of the matter is that my design work has given me life. It has been one of the most fulling parts of my life for sure. Once in a while, a job would come along that was so much more than just a job.

Renee, a classmate of mine from high school, has a child with special needs. Renee and her husband Don have done many amazing things to fill their daughter's life with the experiences all kids love. When her daughter couldn't use the local playground—and when Renee and Don realized there were dozens of other kids who could not either—they didn't complain or wait for the city to do something. They simply went to work telling their story and started raising money for the creation of a more inclusive playground.

Raising money in Boonetown isn't easy, but they did it, at every club, at every church, on the radio, and anywhere else they could be heard. Oh, and they sold thousands of tee shirts. Within a year or so, they had over four hundred thousand dollars.

I could tell that Renee was not excited about the ideas being presented for the park. They were functional, but they weren't fun. While we were talking, an idea was already forming on the movie screen I have in my head and by the time I got home, it was just a matter of putting it on paper.

I felt I had a strong sense of what she wanted, and I knew the playground needed to be bright and colorful and fun, like a theme park. Knowing that many kids with disabilities never get to go to theme parks, I wanted to create that kind of feeling. I immediately knew I wanted a clock tower, and a pavilion, and a cool entry gate, and lots of colorful signage, in addition to all the playground stuff. I wanted there to be a sense that you had arrived at a special place.

I was pleased with my sketch, even though I was pretty sure it would get scaled way back since the design was fairly ambitious. But, considering the amount of work Renee and Don had already put into this project, I still wanted them to see the design and see what might be possible.

I took the sketch to show Renee. Tears formed in her eyes and I knew she loved it. It was a moment I'll never forget. She and her husband both said it was just what they had imagined.

Much to my surprise, they built the park exactly as I had drawn in that original sketch. Complete with the clock tower, and the pavilion, and all the other fun details I had thought of. They would not compromise. So many Boonevillians volunteered their time and energy and money, and we all saw it through to the end.

On opening day, I was teary eyed, too, when I saw

the kids. They were joyful. I was overwhelmed. They had something to call their own. And so did I, even though my reasons were different. For me it was seeing a design vision fully realized. For them it was simply a place to play, at last.

That experience reminded me that good design really can make people's lives better. It showed me how much can be accomplished when people work together with a common goal. To me, good design is much more than just making a space look good. It's about using my abilities to help make the place I live a *better* place to live.

And so far, as I have made my way through this accidental career, luck has been on my side. Like the night I was trapped under the armoire. Luckily, I summoned up enough strength to push it off me just enough to slither out. Then I was just trapped in the basement, but I had a phone down there.

I didn't perish then, but if I had moved my last piece of furniture that night, at least you'd know I went out doing something that I loved.

And just in case, I immediately went to my computer and e-mailed several family members some current photos of myself with the subject line: Obituary Photo.

A Merry Little Christmas

Christmas used to be a very big deal to me. Not so much because of the gifts, but because of all the holiday decorations. It was always about the designer in me.

I was raised in a Catholic household and my mom and dad took Christmas very seriously. In the Catholic faith, the four weeks leading up to Christmas are known as Advent. The church decorates for Advent with pink and purple. No Christmas decorations. None.

The Christmas decorations were never put up in the church until after the last Sunday of Advent was over, and you first saw them when you attended Christmas services. This last-minute decorating did have a nice shock-factor, and there was a high level of anticipation. All of that was fine and good for the church.

But Mom and Dad felt that we should do the same thing at home. They would never let us decorate at home until a week or maybe two until the actual day. I think if Mom had had her way, she would have been fine if we never decorated at all.

But for me all that waiting was torture. I would see decorations up everywhere when we went out shopping and I would beg her to let us put some up at home. No deal. Not even just a few. Especially not lights outside. I think she was afraid the church police would drive by and see lights. My parents went by the rules.

There were two sweet older ladies at our church that always took care of the altars and decorated for the high holy occasions. They were sisters and had never married and were both very dedicated to the church. The ladies even had religious names: Bernadette and Elizabeth. They still lived in the old family home. Of course, it was immaculate, and all the beautiful woodwork and family antiques had been kept in pristine condition. Their brother was a priest at another parish. Bernadette and Elizabeth always decorated the church for Christmas.

These ladies probably only weighed about ninety pounds each. They actually split one egg for breakfast. (A fact I still can't get over since I usually have three myself.) So, the task of lifting all the large plaster nativity figures out from under the back altar was a big chore for them.

One year, since they were friends with my mom, they asked me to help them put up the Christmas decorations. I was happy to help. I was probably twelve or thirteen then, and they taught me all the handed-down procedures for setting up the Nativity, which was done the same way every year without exception.

First, I would have to go up to the third-floor storage room to bring down the sawhorses and plywood and the big wooden stable structure. I would have to set the sawhorses in front of the side altar and then put the huge piece of oval-cut plywood on top. After that, there was a gathered, green skirt to cover the sawhorse legs and two different cloths were layered on top. Then a green garland went around the edge. Another brother of the ladies had made the stable many years before. Bernadette was a wonderful artist and had drawn a scene in chalk that was placed behind the stable and lit with a little hidden lightbulb. When you looked at the nativity, you could see Bethlehem in the distance.

I loved the nativity set. There were many characters, unlike the one we had at home with just a few of the main players that were maybe six inches tall. Of course, Mary and Joseph took center stage, but there were three shepherds, a piccolo player, about twelve sheep figures, an ass, a cow, and a ram with big rounded horns. They were all solid plaster, hand painted and heavy. I was constantly reminded not to drop them, and I never did. The finishing touch was the large angel that hung from a nail right below the roof of the stable, over the baby Jesus. It always bothered me that the baby Jesus figure was almost as big as Mary herself. I'm not sure if this was just for emphasis, since it was his day, or if he was a replacement figure and was just accidentally out of proportion. Then on the Epiphany, (a Catholic feast day celebrated on January sixth) the three kings arrived. They were large beautiful statues with ornate robes, about twenty-four inches tall, and they had a couple of camels in tow to transport their travel gear. Some of the sheep and shepherds had to be removed in order to fit them all in on the plywood base.

Our Parish had an authentic old church building. It was Gothic in design, built in 1887, with soaring arched ceilings. Even as a child, I was amazed that my ancestors were able to design and build something this special in a small town like Boonetown. The people who built the church were mostly poor farmers that worked as volunteers. (Imagine trying to build a church today with volunteer labor.) There were three large altars: two up front on the left and right sides and then the biggest one was at the rear center of the sanctuary. The altars were hand carved by parishioners when the church was built, and each one had three niches for life-sized statues.

My least favorite part of the Christmas decorating process was replacing all the candles. The candles were purchased new every year for Christmas. The church had a set of eighteen, solid-brass, ornate candlesticks that ranged from twenty-four to about thirty-two inches tall. They were very heavy, and placed fairly high up on the three wooden carved altars. My height really was an advantage. The ladies would have me take them all down and then help them place the brand-new beeswax candles in them. Then we would place the brass "followers" on top of the candles to ensure that the candles would burn evenly. (I had never seen followers before or since, come to think of it, but they are little brass caps that fit on the top of the candle with a hole in the top for the wick to stick through. They really add a nice touch to the overall look of the candles too.)

When I was an altar boy, I always hated lighting the candles at midnight mass because we had to use the five-foot-long candle-lighting pole (for lack of a better word) to light all the candles. For regular masses, we only lit some of the candles. But on high holy days we lit them all, including the candelabras (which I also had to retrieve from the third-floor storage room). Those had nine beeswax candles each, complete with followers. If you were lighting the candles, you had about forty to light with the church packed for midnight mass. So, you didn't want to knock any over and set the place on fire. Lots of witnesses.

Next in the decorating process, we would get out the Christmas altar cloths. Basically huge tablecloths made of linen with hand embroidery or crochet along the edges. The set we used at Christmas had sixteen inches of intricately detailed crochet work, all starched and ironed by another dedicated church lady. The church had many sets of altar cloths and these were the most ornate (ok, maybe there was a tie with the Easter set). They were rolled on long tubes to keep them wrinkle free prior to use. Then we would unroll them across each of the three altars and use brass screw-presses to hold them in place.

Lastly, we would place the ferns and the poinsettias. Usually a few dozen red poinsettias had been ordered with the pots wrapped in gold foil paper, finished off with red bows. These were placed on the altars between the huge candle sticks and in front of the ferns. (The ferns were in the background to provide the needed touch of green.) A couple of ladies in the parish grew extra-large Boston ferns in their basement so they would be full and healthy at Christmas.

As I type this, it occurs to me that this is probably why new Christmas decorations have so little appeal to me. I started out with the very best: A forty-piece hand painted nativity, solid brass candlesticks, real beeswax candles, and hand embroidered linen. We had no need for strung Christmas lights because we had candlelight, and we also had fresh flowers. It was all so authentic. And it was breathtaking to walk into midnight mass and see it all magically in place.

The ladies asked for my help all through my high school and college years, and I always enjoyed it. And I enjoyed being with them too. They were becoming less and less able to handle the lifting, and the Christmas and Easter decorating was passed over to me when I got out of college. I was one of the few people that knew all the little details required to put it all together. It was creative and I loved anything creative.

When I was back in the family business in my early twenties, the church building was nearing its one-hundredth anniversary. The church was in poor condition. It had undergone an unflattering renovation during the sixties, and the lighting and mechanical systems needed updating. The church was also in need of plaster repair, painting, and reworking of the altars to bring them up to Vatican II standards...which proved to be quite controversial.

A church committee was formed, and my family's construction business was chosen to do the work. It was a massive undertaking. I was put in charge of the church restoration project. The building was going to be one hundred years old, and we would only have the time between Christmas and the anniversary date in early May to complete the job. No pressure. I am not sure I was qualified but no one else in town was either, and we had consultants from New York guiding us through the design process, so I was excited to take it on.

Of course, there were many opinions about what needed to be done and what should not be touched. But once I started the project, I was pretty laser-focused on that looming deadline and was able to block out most of the clatter. When it was completed, I was incredibly proud of the work that had been done. I learned a lot working with the consultants. I loved the colors they chose. It was understated and elegant, and even the changes that were required by Vatican II were done in a way that most people were pleased with. Since it was my first big renovation project, it gave me some confidence as I tackled new jobs.

I was excited to decorate the sanctuary that first Christmas after the renovation. I kept many of traditional elements so there would be continuity in the décor, and then added some new touches of my own. It was beautiful.

I decorated the church for another twenty years or so, until my parents died. Even though the Catholic Church is no longer part of my life, I have very fond memories of those days I spent preparing that beautiful sanctuary for Christmas. I like tradition. When I was really lucky, my cousin, who was the church organist would be practicing hymns on the big pipe organ while I was working. Those were days when I really felt the Christmas spirit.

When I first had my own home, in my early twenties, I did a lot of Christmas decorating for myself. I was also asked to do a lot of Christmas decorating for clients. I always decorated my mom's house for Christmas, since she never liked to do it. If my sister was home, she helped with decorations at mom's house too, but I still had to do my own home and then the church...throw in a few client's homes and I was getting burnt out quickly.

I think what finally ended my decorating for clients was when this lady called asking me to work on her huge house. It was already the first of November and she wouldn't take no for an answer.

I said, "What kind of decorations are you thinking about?"

And she said, "I want a lot of lights outside, you know like Opryland Hotel."

I said, "You do know they have a crew of one hundred that starts in August, right?"

Then she said, "Well, just do as much as you can."

That's when I realized that I needed some kind of a personal connection to want to do the job. Just doing a big job because it was a big job really had no appeal to me. And that's when I quit Christmas decorating for clients.

To me, if you have to hire someone to come in and put up Christmas decorations for you, you have lost the spirit of the thing. It's about families gathering and decorating the tree together, and getting into big arguments because Dad wants colored lights and Mom wants clear. It's about putting out the ornaments you have collected over a lifetime, not someone bringing in a bunch of color coordinated ones.

It wasn't long before I lost interest in Christmas decorating at my own house. I might put a wreath on the front door, but that was it. Then it got to where I just did the church and helped my mom with hers. I found it amazing how something that meant so much to me as a child could end up meaning so little to me as an adult. I think the fact that I lived alone was a big factor. Decorating the church was giving hundreds of people pleasure, and all our family gathered at Mom's house for the holidays so those efforts were seen as well. But for me, at home alone, looking at Christmas decorations made me sad. Now when I contemplate decorating for Christmas at home, "maybe next year" seems to be my first thought.

Mom had tired of the hassle of Christmas decorations and shopping many years before she died. And I get it. For her, the holiday represented a lot of work that she had to add to her already long list of chores. It was wonderful for all of us. She always did the big traditional spread of our favorite holiday foods. I can only imagine how exhausted she was by the end of Christmas Day. Now I wish we had given her a year-off one year, rather than a new outfit, but I feel pretty sure she would have insisted on doing her Christmas duty anyway. She continued to do all the cooking and the other chores required of the season, until she was too weak from cancer treatments.

Dad never cared much for Christmas, other than singing in the choir. So I guess I got it honest, my diminishing Christmas spirit.

I've been thinking about some of these Christmas memories this year, the year of the COVID Christmas. Seems like this pandemic has given us all some time and a reason to pause and to think about things that mean something, or have meant something, in our lives. Missing Christmas celebrations really doesn't bother me at all because mine are usually pretty simple these days. After my parents died, I began hosting Thanksgiving at my house and my brother would have Christmas at his, and it has worked just fine. As I approach sixty, having a big formal dinner or opening a lot of gifts means little to me now. A year like this makes you realize that the real gifts are the people: The friends and the family that are there every day, not just on Christmas.

My family and friends are not the "huggy" type, or the type to throw out "I love you's" at the end of every phone call. But the friends and family I have in Boonetown are the type that will show up for me anytime I ask and often even if I don't ask. Some of my friends double as helpers on my design jobs, helping to haul, unpack, assemble, hold, lift, and clean up. They would work for free if I let them, just because they like seeing what I am up to on my projects. We have the best time. I am very lucky.

And during the crazy times, having people that you can really count on to always pick up the phone, always listen, and always care, keeps you sane. They are not only there for me, they are there for anyone they know that needs help, and that's what makes them all really special.

I've never really fit in here in Boonetown and I guess I've never really tried. I've always been pretty content to be an odd duck. I've always thought I would have fit in better in a large city, but that's not how it happened. I could have moved away, and maybe I should have, but the family business was here and it seemed like the right thing to do at the time, so I stayed.

It's a small town, like most small towns, all the activities are based around family life, like little league, school activities and sports. Single people don't have a lot of social opportunities. But thankfully, I found a bunch of cohorts that don't really fit in either. That's the real gift. That's a gift I want to keep opening year after year. Holidays will come and go. Hopefully COVID will go soon, too, and things will get back to normal. But whatever normal looks like in the future, I'll value my family and friendships even more.

Made in the USA
Columbia, SC
16 February 2022